# TABLE
# MOUNTAIN

## A NATURAL HISTORY

To Philippa and Kathy

# TABLE MOUNTAIN

## A NATURAL HISTORY

## Anton Pauw and Steven Johnson

Endorsed by the Botanical Society
of South Africa

FERNWOOD
PRESS

# The Sponsor

The publisher gratefully acknowledges the financial contribution
made by Old Mutual to the publication of this book.

FERNWOOD
PRESS

P O Box 15344 • 8018 Vlaeberg • South Africa
website: www.fernwoodpress.co.za

Registration no. 90/04463/07

First published 1999
Reprinted 2002

Edited by *Sue Matthews*
Proofread by *Tessa Kennedy*
Concept design by *Joanne Simpson*
Designed and typeset by *Abdul Amien*
Cover design by *Willem Jordaan*
Maps by *ComputaMaps* and *Red Roof Design*
Production control by *Abdul Latief (Bunny) Gallie*
Repro co-ordinator *Andrew De Kock*

Reproduction by Unifoto (Pty) Ltd, Cape Town
Printed and bound by Tien Wah Press (Pte) Ltd, Singapore
Collectors' edition bound by Peter Carstens, Johannesburg

Standard edition ISBN 1 874950 43 1
Collectors' edition ISBN 1 874950 44 X

# Contents

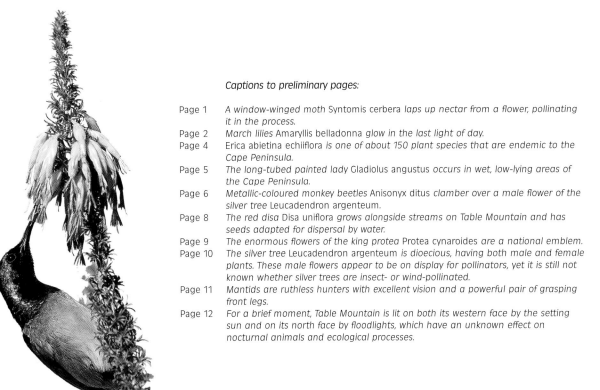

*Captions to preliminary pages:*

Page 1  *A window-winged moth* Syntomis cerbera *laps up nectar from a flower, pollinating it in the process.*

Page 2  *March lilies* Amaryllis belladonna *glow in the last light of day.*

Page 4  Erica abietina echiiflora *is one of about 150 plant species that are endemic to the Cape Peninsula.*

Page 5  *The long-tubed painted lady* Gladiolus angustus *occurs in wet, low-lying areas of the Cape Peninsula.*

Page 6  *Metallic-coloured monkey beetles* Anisonyx ditus *clamber over a male flower of the silver tree* Leucadendron argenteum.

Page 8  *The red disa* Disa uniflora *grows alongside streams on Table Mountain and has seeds adapted for dispersal by water.*

Page 9  *The enormous flowers of the king protea* Protea cynaroides *are a national emblem.*

Page 10  *The silver tree* Leucadendron argenteum *is dioecious, having both male and female plants. These male flowers appear to be on display for pollinators, yet it is still not known whether silver trees are insect- or wind-pollinated.*

Page 11  *Mantids are ruthless hunters with excellent vision and a powerful pair of grasping front legs.*

Page 12  *For a brief moment, Table Mountain is lit on both its western face by the setting sun and on its north face by floodlights, which have an unknown effect on nocturnal animals and ecological processes.*

**OLD MUTUAL** sponsored the first edition of this publication in 1999 and is delighted to support this reprint in 2002 as a *Proudly South African* company

**Roddy Sparks**
Managing Director
Old Mutual South Africa Limited
Cape Town

*July 2002*

# Foreword

The majestic profile of Table Mountain, flanked by Devil's Peak and Lion's Head, is one of the world's most famous landmarks. For many centuries it has been a source of almost mystical inspiration for visitors to Cape Town. Even those who live and work in its shadow every day, cannot help but feel its power. For those privileged to set foot on the sandstone slopes, a new world opens – a world even more awe-inspiring than Table Mountain's famous profile.

The Table Mountain chain is, above all, a living monument to the wonders of biodiversity – on a scale not seen elsewhere on this planet. One can only marvel at the celebration of life on the mountain, in all its glorious forms, and which have been so skilfully captured in the pages of this magnificent book.

The authors, Anton Pauw and Steven Johnson, are two young scientists who have spent many years uncovering the secrets of Table Mountain. Not only have they both been recognised in academic circles for their ground-breaking work in the fields of animal-plant interaction and pollination biology, but both are also highly talented and accomplished nature photographers. This blend of experience, knowledge and creative skills has produced a truly unique work – a work that tells an exciting and very special story about a mountain where many thousands of life forms all have their place, all interdependent on each other for their common survival.

As fascinating as this story is, there is more, for in its telling there is the underlying message that sharing in this very special place on earth brings with it the responsibility for its conservation – a responsibility which rests not only with Capetonians, but also with the entire country and, indeed, the world. It is in this context that the Botanical Society of South Africa has decided to endorse this publication. It is the first time that the Society, founded in 1913, has taken this step – the case for doing so was indeed a compelling one.

I am greatly honoured to present this foreword in the conviction that past presidents of the Society who are no longer with us, namely, the late Sirs J.H. de Villiers and James Rose Innes, Messrs Duncan Baxter and Dudley D'Ewes, and Professors E.A.C.L.E. Schelpe and W.P.U. Jackson, would have looked favourably on the Council of 1999 who, on the eve of the new millennium, voted unanimously for the Botanical Society's official endorsement of this important publication. May this also be a source of inspiration to our 30 000 members worldwide, and indeed to every reader of this book, to make the transition from seeing ourselves not only as the current beneficiaries of the rich natural beauty of Table Mountain, but also as the active custodians of this treasure trove of botanical diversity.

**Adv. Abri B. Meiring**
*President of the Botanical Society of South Africa*

Cape Town · July 1999

# Preface

Anyone who has stood on the summit of Table Mountain is left with an indelible impression of the grandeur of its landscapes. Not everyone is as impressed by the plants and animals that they encounter, and few would believe that the Cape Peninsula has one of the world's greatest concentrations of unique plant and animal life. At a glance, the vegetation seems somewhat dull, and the animals scarce.

But in the miniature world among the bushes lurk unseen creatures fiercer than lion, stranger than giraffe and more graceful than gazelle. On the Serengeti plain of a leaf's lower surface they graze, hunt, kill, deceive, escape, mate and give birth. A robberfly captures its aerial prey, while a butterfly eagerly probes the depths of a disa for nectar. Much of the floral diversity is expressed on an equally minute scale. Here life celebrates in a profusion of inconspicuous heaths and diminutive orchids, their true beauty revealed only when examined at close range.

We hope that the text and photographs in this book will bring into focus some aspects of the natural history of the Cape Peninsula that we have encountered, and serve as an introduction to this secret world. It is a chronicle of our own journeys of discovery as we have walked and climbed the slopes of the mountain and studied its plants and animals. The chapters of this book explore various themes of natural history. We concentrate on the dynamic interactions between plants and animals – the web of relationships that holds all of this life together – and describe the influence of fire, weather and geology.

The idea to write this book was born several years ago when we discovered that we shared a common love for Table Mountain and its natural inhabitants. Our trips up the mountain became more frequent and gained a greater sense of purpose. Eventually, the project became an all-consuming passion. Attempts were made to find and photograph the most obscure and elusive subjects. Some appear or flower for only a week or two every decade, and then only in one or two locations, and only if the weather is right. Many days went by waiting in a hide to photograph a rameron pigeon, while entire nights were spent waiting for a moth to visit a particular flower.

Although we have endeavoured to observe and capture on film the most important, interesting, bizarre and beautiful creatures of the Cape Peninsula, there are still some subjects that have remained out of our reach. We did not find the white cave peripatus nor the pollinator of the drip disa, but half of the joy in the pursuit of natural history is derived from the knowledge that so many natural things remain rare and unseen. Our hope is that this book will stimulate you to discover more of the secrets of Table Mountain for yourself.

**Anton Pauw · Steven Johnson**
July 1999

# Acknowledgements

Writing a natural history for one of the world's most important biodiversity hotspots is a somewhat daunting task. It requires specialised knowledge of such a range of subjects that in a lifetime one could never learn all that there is to know. In researching this book we often had to rely on the expertise of others.

Among these we owe a special debt to our friends and colleagues in the Botany Department at the University of Cape Town. William Bond encouraged this "deviation" from our research work and shared his insight especially on the ecology of fire. Peter Linder, Terry Trinder-Smith and Pat Lorber from the Bolus Herbarium helped with identification of plants and Terry supplied the new estimates of plant endemism. Richard Cowling and Jeremy Midgley made valuable comments on early drafts of some sections.

In the Zoology Department, Mike Picker and Charles Griffiths gave generously of their vast experience of the natural history of the Cape Peninsula, while Jenny Jarvis fuelled our interest in small mammals. George Branch has been a long-time and valued supporter of this project. Christian Boix-Hinzen, Chris Lotz, Callan Cohen and Ross Wanless passed some of their practical ornithological experience and infectious enthusiasm onto us, while Andrew Jenkins led the tireless pursuit of the peregrine falcon. Mark Cooper, John Hoffman, Norma Sharratt and Kate Snaddon helped with the naming of animals and shared their specialised knowledge.

For the difficult task of identifying insects we relied on the collections of the South African Museum and received a great deal of assistance from Simon van Noort, Hamish Robertson and Vincent Whitehead.

Bill Branch, Marius Burger, Mike Cherry and Atherton de Villiers had the answers to many herpetological questions, while Dave Gaynor and Ruth Kansky helped with current information on the baboons of the Cape Peninsula.

At the Kirstenbosch Botanical Garden we are indebted to Dion Kotze, Hubert Kurzweil, Tony Rebelo, Dee Snijman, Kim Steiner and Ernst van Jaarsveld. We are grateful for the information or assistance provided by Paul Britton, Hennie Homann and James Jackelman from the Cape Peninsula National Park and by Pieter Kruger from the Cape Metropolitan Council. Dalton Gibbs and Clifford Dorse introduced us to the botanical rarities of the Rondevlei Nature Reserve.

Many people assisted us in our quest to photograph some of the more elusive subjects of this book, from kukumakrankas to porcupines. Among these are "Bossie" and Allet Bosman, Betty Dwight, Mike Fraser and Liz McMahon, Ivan Groenhof, Alan Heath, Norman Larsen and Brian Vorster, while Bill Liltved took us to see some of the rare orchids that are illustrated here.

Philippa Allen, Nick Lindenberg and David McKelly helped in the production of the vegetation map. The forest distribution was meticulously plotted by Doug Euston-Brown.

We are grateful to Dane Gerneke, Miranda Waldon, Trevor Sewell and Mohamed Jaffer of the Electron Microscope Unit at UCT for their patience and assistance with mites and bird tongues.

Sandy Smuts, the administrative assistant of the Botany Department, as well as Tessa Davies and Danielle du Toit, the librarians of the Bolus and Niven libraries, could always help with our never-ending requests and queries.

Our parents, Charl and Jennifer Pauw and Mike and Des Johnson, nurtured our interest in the natural world and encouraged us throughout the production of this book. Christien Malan and Pieter Labuschagne provided Anton with a basecamp on the slopes of the mountain, and were companions and mentors on journeys of discovery. Anton is grateful to Fotini Babaletakis for her help during the early stages of this project.

Finally, we are very grateful to Peter Borchert who believed in this project and got the machinery for its production into motion, to Pieter and Pam Struik, Bunny Gallie, Sue Matthews and Abdul Amien for making our dream a reality and to Abri Meiring of Old Mutual who showed such enthusiasm for this project.

# Introduction

At the south-western corner of Africa, where a sharp tooth of land juts out into the great Atlantic Ocean, Table Mountain rises majestically from the sea. It is a flat-topped massif, often shrouded in swirling mists, and its unparalleled biological riches make it one of the most celebrated natural places on earth.

At just over a thousand metres, the height of Table Mountain is modest, yet it ranks in status alongside such famous African giants as Kilimanjaro and Mount Kenya. Viewed from the surrounding sea or the vast sand flats below, it appears to loom over the city of Cape Town, an effect exaggerated when the summit is draped in clouds and the slopes are dark and foreboding.

Flanking the mountain on either side are the impressive formations of Lion's Head and Devil's Peak. Seafarers viewed this trio of peaks with awe as well as relief, for their familiar contours signalled the end of a long voyage from Europe. Behind Table Mountain a range of smaller mountains forms a chain along the length of the Cape Peninsula. Its rocky profile calls to mind a sleeping dragon, with Table Mountain as its head and the Peninsula mountain range as its spiny tail, gradually flattening out before it plunges into the sea at Cape Point.

Close-up, the mountain's eroded sandstone surface and strange weather-beaten plants give little hint of anything out of the ordinary. Yet Table Mountain is renowned among biologists for its staggering biological diversity. There are 2 285 plant species crammed onto the Peninsula, and most of these are found on Table Mountain. In fact, this tiny strip of land has more plant species than Sweden, a thousand times larger.

Most of Table Mountain is clothed in fynbos, the quintessential plant life of the Cape that is found nowhere else on earth. Its unique qualities were considered deserving of its recognition as one of the world's six floral kingdoms. But although the mountain is justly famous as a botanical paradise, it is also home to many animals, some of them carrying out essential duties for plants, such as pollination and seed dispersal.

Clearly, Table Mountain is one of the "hotspots" of biological diversity on the planet. This is all the more remarkable given the bustling city of some three million inhabitants at its foot.

We begin this book with an overall perspective on the mountain. Later, in the following chapters, we take a closer look at its natural inhabitants. Many have rather private lives, but with a little bit of coaxing they have been persuaded to give up their secrets.

## FYNBOS, FOREST AND RENOSTERVELD

The rich diversity of plants on Table Mountain made a powerful impression on the early explorers. After climbing the slopes of Lion's Head in 1810, the English naturalist William Burchell compared the sight to a "botanic garden, neglected and left to grow to a state of nature; so great was the variety everywhere to be met with". Earlier, his Swedish counterpart Anders Sparrman had written of the "pleasure enjoyed by a botanist who finds all at once so rich a collection of unknown, rare and beautiful vernal flowers in so unfrequented a part of the world".

Today, botanists recognise three kinds of indigenous vegetation on Table Mountain. Fynbos covers the greatest area, including the upper plateau, while patches of forest cling to the south- and east-facing slopes and remnants of renosterveld are found on Signal Hill.

It was the fynbos that evoked the poetic descriptions of Burchell and Sparrman. The word fynbos is a Dutch derivative of "fine bush", describing the vegetation's small leaves, which are also prickly and rough-edged, as many a hiker with scratched and

*OPPOSITE: The nutrient-poor, sandstone soils of the mountain's upper plateau support a surprising diversity of reed-like restios and heath-like ericas.*
**1** *A Table Mountain icon, the elusive ghost frog* Heleophryne rosei *occurs only in a small area on the eastern and southern slopes.*
**2** *Cradling the city of Cape Town, Devil's Peak, Table Mountain and Lion's Head shrug off a blanket of mist.*
**3** *The golden conebush* Leucadendron laureolum *adorns the slopes of Noordhoek Peak.*

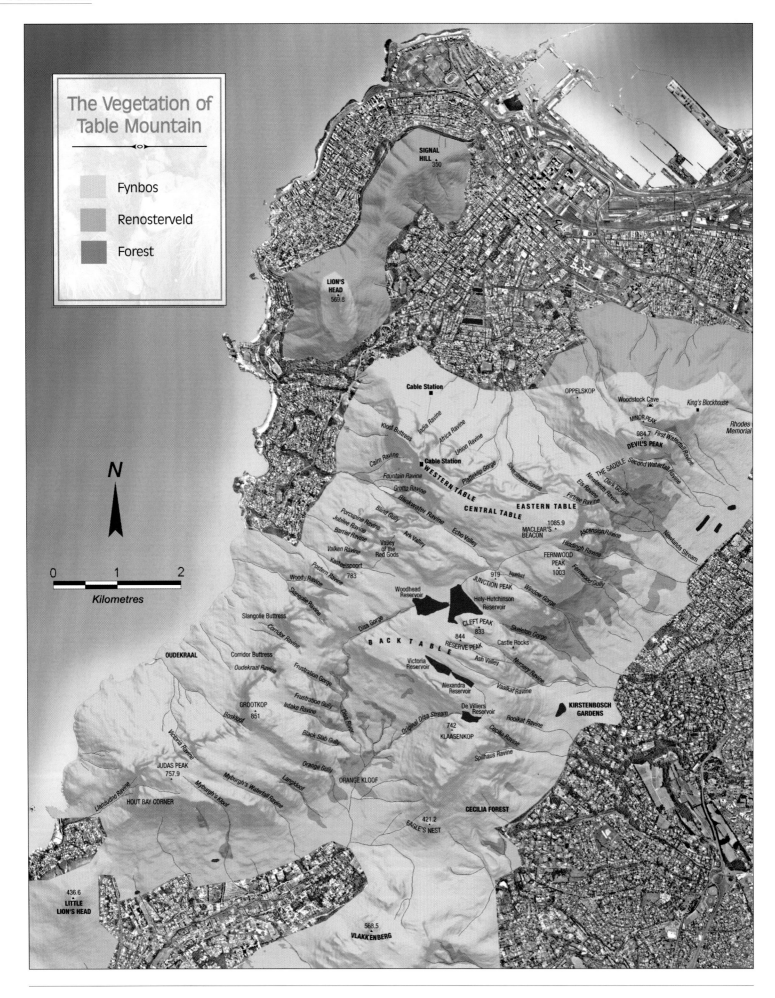

## The Vegetation of
## Table Mountain

◄─────◄◊►─────►

- Fynbos
- Renosterveld
- Forest

N

0        1        2
Kilometres

SIGNAL
HILL
350

LION'S
HEAD
569.8

Cable Station

OPPELSKOP

Woodstock Cave

King's Blockhouse

MINOR PEAK

Rhodes
Memorial

Kloof Buttress

India Ravine

Africa Ravine

Union Ravine

984.7   First Waterfall Ravine

DEVIL'S PEAK

Cairn Ravine

Cable Station

Platteklip Gorge

Saddleback Ravine

THE SADDLE   Second Waterfall Ravine

Fountain Ravine

WESTERN TABLE

Newlands Ravine

Dark Gorge

Els Ravine

Grotto Ravine

Firtree Ravine

Blind Gully

Blinkwater Ravine

CENTRAL TABLE

EASTERN TABLE

Porcupine Ravine

Ark Valley

Echo Valley

1085.9

MACLEAR'S
BEACON

Ascension Ravine

Newlands Stream

Jubilee Ravine

Barrier Ravine

Valken Ravine

Valley
of the
Red Gods

Hiddingh Ravine

FERNWOOD
PEAK
1003

Kasteelspoort

Postern Ravine

783

919

JUNCTION PEAK

Aqueduct

Window Gorge

Fernwood Gully

Woody Ravine

Woodhead
Reservoir

Hely-Hutchinson
Reservoir

Slangolie Ravine

Slangolie Buttress

Disa Gorge

CLEFT PEAK
833

Skeleton Gorge

Corridor Ravine

B A C K   T A B L E

844

RESERVE PEAK

Castle Rocks

OUDEKRAAL

Corridor Buttress

Victoria
Reservoir

Ash Valley

Nursery Ravine

Oudekraal Ravine

Frustration Gorge

Alexandra
Reservoir

Vaalkat Ravine

KIRSTENBOSCH
GARDENS

GROOTKOP
851

Intake Ravine

Frustration Gully

Disa River

De Villiers
Reservoir

Rooikat Ravine

Boskloof

Original Disa Stream

742

Cecilia Ravine

Black Slab Gully

KLAASENKOP

Spilhaus Ravine

Victoria Ravine

Orange Gully

JUDAS PEAK
757.9

Myburgh's Waterfall Ravine

Langkloof

ORANGE KLOOF

CECILIA FOREST

Llandudno Ravine

Myburgh's Kloof

HOUT BAY CORNER

421.2

EAGLE'S NEST

436.6
LITTLE
LION'S HEAD

568.5

VLAKKENBERG

even bleeding skin can testify. In botanical-speak the fynbos is termed "sclerophyllous" because of these hard leaves, but its gentler side is revealed in the heady aroma of its buchu shrubs and its vivid and saturated colours. In the clear light after a winter storm, a fynbos-covered slope is a rich palette of yellow leucadendrons, green shrubs and brown restios.

Yet fynbos is often a disappointment to the uninitiated, especially those more familiar with the lush green meadows of Europe. Lady Anne Barnard, on reaching the top of Table Mountain in 1797, complained that there "was nothing of that luxuriancy of verdure and foliage, flower or herbage, described by travellers; there were roots and some flowers, and a beautiful heath on the edge of the rocks, but the soil was cold, swampy and mossy, covered in general with half an inch of water, rushes growing in it, and sprinkled all over with white pebbles".

Why, then, is fynbos so highly regarded among botanists? The large number of species (more than 8 500) is part of the answer, but the main reason is that nearly 70 per cent of these species are endemic to the south-western Cape, which means that they are found nowhere else in the world. The Cape Peninsula itself has about 160 endemic plant species – the highest endemism for any area of similar size in the world.

The Cape Floral Kingdom stretches from Clanwilliam in the north to Humansdorp in the east, forming an L-shaped belt about 1 000 kilometres long and 200 kilometres wide. Table Mountain is the perfect showcase for this smallest but most fascinating of plant kingdoms. Visiting botanists are often amazed by the differences in plant species composition from one slope to another, and it is this variation over small distances that makes a walk on the mountain so exciting. Species confined to narrow habitats include the drip disa *Disa longicornis*, found only in south-facing rock clefts above 600 metres, and the gangly *Erica urna-viridis*, which occurs on the top of the Muizenberg mountains and nowhere else in the world. But not all fynbos species are quite so particular about their

habitat; some, like blombos *Metalasia muricata* and the fire heath *Erica cerinthoides*, are widespread, the latter even occurring beyond the Cape.

The plant communities in fynbos are seldom dominated by one species. A patch of fynbos vegetation will usually contain a mix of proteas, reed-like

*OPPOSITE: Three kinds of indigenous vegetation occur on Table Mountain. Fynbos covers the largest area, including the upper plateau, while patches of forest cling to the south- and east-facing slopes and renosterveld is found on Signal Hill and Devil's Peak.*

*The 104 erica species that occur on the Cape Peninsula have typically small, hard leaves, like those of* Erica plukenetii *(1), but their delicate flowers vary greatly in shape and colour, and in the structure of the anthers. In this species the long*

*anthers are fused into a ring that erupts with a shower of pollen when probed by a sunbird. Also bird-pollinated, the fire heath* Erica cerinthoides *(2) is widespread, but most species have more localised distributions.* Erica urna-viridis *(3) and* Erica abietina *(4), for example, are confined to small areas of the Cape Peninsula.*

*5 The geometric arrangement of leaves on the stem of* Saltera sarcocolla *is characteristic of the Penaeaceae, one of five plant families unique to the Cape Floral Kingdom.*

restios and fine-leafed ericas, as well as some of the aromatic buchus and pelargoniums, delicate gladioli, and sedges. The diversity in a small area can be staggering – 121 species were once recorded in a plot of 10 square metres!

The reed-like plants belonging to the family Restionaceae are perhaps the most characteristic fynbos plants. Their thin, wiry stems, resembling the jointed sections of a tent pole, are still used for thatching, although not as extensively as when the plants were common on the Cape Flats. Shallow root systems allow them to thrive in the poor soils of the fynbos, from dry slopes to marshes. Much of the boggy summit plateau of Table Mountain is covered by dense stands of the endemic restio *Thamnochortus nutans.*

Restios have separate sexes, so it is easy to mistake male and female plants for different species. Their flowers are dull-coloured, as they are wind-pollinated and so have no need for bright colours to attract insects. The Restionaceae is thought to be one of the oldest of the Cape flora's families as some of its members are also found in Australia, which drifted away from the Cape more than 120 million years ago.

**1** Pelargonium cucullatum tabulare *is one of 200 naturally occurring members of the genus in South Africa. These species are the wild ancestors of the "geraniums" that grace the flower boxes of Europe.*
**2** *Restios, such as this* Chondropetalum mucronatum, *are the dominant plants on the summit plateau of Table Mountain.*
**3** *Superficially resembling a daisy,* Staavia glutinosa *is a rare Table Mountain endemic that belongs to the Bruniaceae, a family restricted to the Cape.*

In places on Table Mountain, the fynbos is reminiscent of the Scottish heathlands, owing to the abundance of fine-leafed shrubs belonging to the genus *Erica*. This is the most diverse genus on the Cape Peninsula, with over 100 species boasting flowers of almost every shape and colour imaginable, from small pink goblets to long yellow tubes probed by the beaks of sunbirds. The leaves are tightly folded to prevent excessive water loss in summer, and the roots have fungal partners, known as mycorrhizae, which assist in obtaining scarce mineral nutrients, such as phosphorus and nitrogen. Table Mountain has several endemic ericas, including *Erica pilulifera* and *Erica empetrina*.

But for many people, fynbos is synonymous with the protea family. The largest genera on Table Mountain are *Protea*, *Leucospermum*, *Leucadendron* and *Serruria*. The king protea *Protea cynaroides*, its flower a national emblem, is still quite common on some of the eastern slopes of the mountain. The waboom *Protea nitida* grows to the size of a small tree, so it was one of the few fynbos species that could be used for timber and was heavily exploited in the past. Pincushions are represented by the stately *Leucospermum*

4

*Aptly named after the legendary god Proteus, who was able to take many forms, members of the genus* Protea *range from the tree-like waboom* Protea nitida (**4**), *heavily exploited in the past for timber, and the shrubby* Protea speciosa (**5**), *to the diminutive* Protea scolymocephala (**6**), *confined to a few small populations on the Cape Peninsula. Less familiar members of the protea family* (Proteaceae) *include the creeping pincushion* Leucospermum hypophyllocarpodendron (**7**), *and the Peninsula-endemic* Diastella divaricata (**8**), *a low, sprawling shrub with minute flowers.*

5

6

7

8

*conocarpodendron* and diminutive *Leucospermum hypophyllocarpodendron,* which forms a straggling carpet close to the ground.

Leucadendrons usually add a warm glow to fynbos vegetation because of their yellowish leaves, but *Leucadendron argenteum* is remarkable for its metallic silver leaves. Aptly called the silver tree, for it is one of the few fynbos plants that can really be considered a tree, it is a Table Mountain icon. The leaves' silvery sheen is believed to protect them from the heat of summer by reflecting sunlight.

*The silver tree* Leucadendron argenteum *(1) is endemic to the Cape Peninsula, as is the conebush* Leucadendron strobilinum *(2), its female flowers serving to attract insects that courier pollen from male plants nearby.*
*3 The magnificent, bowl-shaped flowerheads of the king protea* Protea cynaroides *are a national emblem.*

Nerine, Brunsvigia and Amaryllis. Finally, some of the rarest and most beautiful wildflowers on Table Mountain are the orchids, many of them seen only after fire. There are more than 100 orchid species on the Cape Peninsula, although many people are surprised to learn that these exquisite plants flourish in the harsh fynbos landscape.

The intense colour and light of the fynbos seems a world apart from the muted tones of the forest. Tall trees with spreading branches block out the sunlight and the forest floor, covered with a litter of

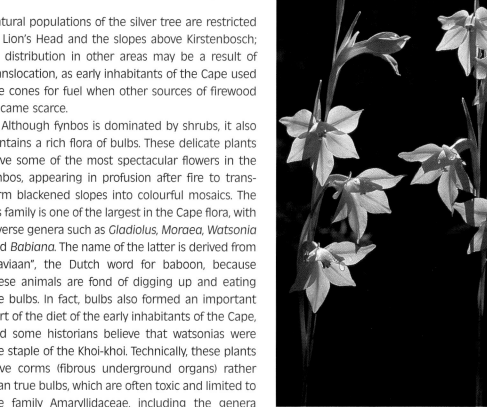

Natural populations of the silver tree are restricted to Lion's Head and the slopes above Kirstenbosch; its distribution in other areas may be a result of translocation, as early inhabitants of the Cape used the cones for fuel when other sources of firewood became scarce.

Although fynbos is dominated by shrubs, it also contains a rich flora of bulbs. These delicate plants have some of the most spectacular flowers in the fynbos, appearing in profusion after fire to transform blackened slopes into colourful mosaics. The iris family is one of the largest in the Cape flora, with diverse genera such as Gladiolus, Moraea, Watsonia and Babiana. The name of the latter is derived from "baviaan", the Dutch word for baboon, because these animals are fond of digging up and eating the bulbs. In fact, bulbs also formed an important part of the diet of the early inhabitants of the Cape, and some historians believe that watsonias were the staple of the Khoi-khoi. Technically, these plants have corms (fibrous underground organs) rather than true bulbs, which are often toxic and limited to the family Amaryllidaceae, including the genera

4 Wurmbea hiemalis is a bulb plant endemic to the Cape Peninsula, but some members of the genus occur in Australia. This species flowers after fire in moist areas.
5 Smaller than the familiar garden variety, Agapanthus africanus is an indigenous fynbos species.
6 A typical renosterveld species, Gladiolus watsonius prefers the rich clay soils of Signal Hill and Devil's Peak. This species was long considered to belong to a separate genus because of its unusual flowers, which are adapted for bird pollination.

# The diversity of disas

There are more than 50 species of *Disa* on the Cape Peninsula. The flowers on this page are just a few of the species that have been recorded..

Many other plant groups have also proliferated in the Cape region, including the heaths (there are more than 100 *Erica* species on the Cape Peninsula alone), legumes such as *Aspalathus*, and irises such as *Gladiolus* and *Moraea*. Why have so many plant species evolved in this corner of Africa? Some botanists believe that there are an unusually high number of habitat "niches" for plants in the rugged Cape mountains. Others argue that the diversity of flowering plants is an adaptation to the variety of insect pollinators, including butterflies, moths, bees, and even horseflies! The debate is likely to continue for decades to come.

1 *Disa tenuifolia*
2 *Disa maculata*
3 *Disa filicornis*
4 *Disa glandulosa*
5 *Disa harveiana*
6 *Disa lugens*
7 *Disa racemosa*
8 *Disa graminifolia*
9 *Disa atricapilla*
10 *Disa longicornu*

rotting leaves, is cool and damp. On Table Mountain, forest patches cling precariously to the moist ravines and slopes of the eastern buttresses, but a much larger forest occurs at Orange Kloof, further round the mountain. Under siege by colonialists for hundreds of years, the forests have survived and now flourish as protected areas.

Renosterveld is the third type of vegetation on Table Mountain. Compared with fynbos and forest, it occupies a very small area, but contains many rare and threatened species. Renosterveld once covered vast tracts of the Western Cape lowlands, but is now found mainly in isolated patches, such as those on the lower slopes of Devil's Peak and Signal Hill. Because it occurs on rich clay soils that are also ideal for agriculture, most renosterveld has been ploughed up and replaced with wheat fields and vineyards. Even before the advent of modern agriculture, early Khoi-khoi pastoralists discovered that renosterveld was able to be converted into grasslands by regular burning.

Renosterveld can be recognised by the ubiquitous presence of the "renosterbos" *Elytropappus rhinocerotis*, a rather drab, grey shrub with tiny leaves. Restios, proteas and ericas hardly feature here. In spring, the renosterveld is frequently carpeted with flowers, including those of many bulbous species.

## CREATURES GREAT AND SMALL

Many visitors to Table Mountain expect to see large herds of animals grazing in the fynbos. Instead they find themselves in a peaceful world of flowers swaying in the wind, with the only animals in sight a chattering sunbird or a bee at work in a flower. Is this natural, or has something gone wrong?

The large animals recorded by early settlers were found mostly in the renosterveld of the lowlands, where the soils are more fertile. It is even plausible that the name "renosterveld" was derived from the black rhinos found grazing on the fertile plains north of Table Mountain. But there were never thundering herds of game on the mountain itself, only small antelope such as klipspringer, duiker and grysbok. They can survive on the tough, nutrient-poor leaves of the fynbos, and some still occur on Table Mountain. However, the chief mammalian herbivore in fynbos is the rock hyrax or dassie, a much smaller, hoofed creature distantly related

*1 From his high vantage point a dassie* Procavia capensis *surveys the rocky summit of Table Mountain, keeping a watchful eye out for predatory black eagles.*

*2 Peering cautiously from a tangled mat of water plants,* Afrana fuscigula *is probably the most common frog in the streams of Table Mountain.*

*3 The elusive and nocturnal Cape grysbok* Raphicerus melanotis *is seldom seen on the Cape Peninsula, although it is relatively common.*

*4 With a view of False Bay, a young male baboon* Papio ursinus *takes a break from the time-consuming business of fynbos foraging. He belongs to one of about seven troops that roam the southern part of the Peninsula mountain chain.*

*1 After a hard day's fishing, African penguins* Spheniscus demersus *return to their nests at Boulders Beach.*
*2 A special find for the birdwatcher, the Cape siskin* Pseudochloroptila tottus *is a fynbos endemic.*
*3 The helmeted guineafowl* Numida meleagris *is a recent arrival on the Peninsula.*
*4 Redwing starlings* Onychognathus morio *nest in the cliffs on Table Mountain.*

Of the six fynbos endemics, only the Cape sugarbird, orangebreasted sunbird and Cape siskin are found on the Cape Peninsula. The remaining three, the Cape rockjumper, Victorin's warbler and protea canary, occur on the neighbouring mountains of the Hottentots Holland, but are absent from apparently suitable habitat on the Peninsula. It might be that these species never colonised the Peninsula, or that it is too small an island of habitat to sustain them in the long term, despite periodic colonisation. A large fire, for example, could wipe out most of the suitable habitat for protea canaries on the Peninsula.

Helmeted guineafowl and hadeda ibis until recently did not occur on the Peninsula, but agricultural development has encouraged their spread. These two species seldom venture far into undisturbed fynbos, although guineafowl seem able to survive on the richer pickings in the renosterveld on Signal Hill and Tygerberg. Even in semi-natural environments, both species depend on tall alien trees as night-time roosts. Alien trees are also favoured by some forest-living species, particularly the forest canary, which was first recorded on Table Mountain in 1981, having spread from isolated natural forests to the east by way of plantations and stands of invasive aliens.

The endangered African or jackass penguin – the continent's only penguin – is another that has benefited from the presence of man on the Peninsula. The extermination of large predators has allowed these penguins, which normally only breed on offshore islands, to colonise the coast. In 1985 the first pairs arrived on Boulders Beach, and today the thriving colony is a major tourist attraction.

For birdwatchers, perhaps the biggest "tick" is the rare Knysna warbler, which is fairly common in the dense understorey of forests on the eastern slopes of Table Mountain. Here it skulks about, resembling a chocolate-brown rodent rather than a bird, but it comes into its own with its unmistakable call, shattering the silence of the forest with a cascade of clear notes. The Cape Peninsula is home to about a hundred pairs.

Nevertheless, the Peninsula is by no means a birdwatcher's Mecca. In some senses it is a botanical paradise and zoological desert – the diversity of plants is not nearly equalled by animals. To appreciate Table Mountain's animal life we need to take a step closer into the Lilliputian world beneath the shrubs. Here, life teems among the leaves and flowers. Ants drag seeds into their nests, bees collect pollen, and secretive birds hunt quietly for tiny insects. These daily rituals have been taking place for centuries, largely unaffected by man's influence.

to elephants. It occurs in abundance on the rock faces of the mountain, partly owing to the scarcity of predators.

The only remaining large predators on the mountain are caracal and genets, the rest having been exterminated by man. The last lion was shot in 1802, but leopards persisted until the mid-nineteenth century.

Table Mountain has never had a particularly rich bird fauna and only a few species have vanished, notably the Cape vulture, which occurred until the end of the eighteenth century.

# The lost flora of the suburbs

In 1772, when Carl Thunberg stood on the eastern buttress of Table Mountain and gazed over the Cape Flats, he saw nothing but a few orderly farms and vast sandy tracts covered in heath. Today little remains of the original natural vegetation, sprawling housing developments and alien plants having taken its place. Names like Rondebosch, Wynberg and Salt River scribbled onto yellowing herbarium sheets are an eerie reminder that these present-day suburbs were once the stomping ground of botanists. Dried plant specimens are all that remain of a vanished flora.

A few patches of undeveloped land remain scattered among the suburbs. Rondebosch Common, despite having been used over the centuries as a campground for the military, a grazing field for the local parish and a cricket field, is a preserve to about 200 indigenous plant species. One of these is the legendary

kukumakranka *Gethyllis afra*, a member of the amaryllis family, which was once common on the flats below the mountain, but has now been eliminated from most of its former habitat. Its edible fruits smell like strawberries and, according to Thunberg, were "held in great esteem by the ladies". Nowadays the plants are less appreciated and unwittingly trampled underfoot by people walking their dogs on the Common.

Orchids used to be widespread on the Cape Flats, but today species like *Disa draconis* and *Disa lugens* face an uncertain future in small fragments of land. Some have vanished from the area altogether, such as the magnificent orchid *Disa barbata*, which now survives only as a few individuals in a reserve near Malmesbury that is being choked by alien plants. Similar sad tales exist for almost every other plant that once made its home on the Cape Flats.

**1** The rising tide of urbanisation has all but obliterated the lowland vegetation of the Cape Peninsula and Cape Flats.
**2** Close to extinction on the Cape Peninsula, Moraea elsiae survives as a handful of individuals on the sandy flats in the centre of Kenilworth Racecourse and at Rondevlei Nature Reserve.
**3** Rondebosch Common provides a small refuge for approx-
imately 200 lowland plant species, such as this Ixia monadelpha.
**4** Until its recent rediscovery in the centre of Milnerton Racecourse, Disa lugens was thought to be extinct on the Cape Flats, where it was once abundant.
**5** The Khoi name kukumakranka is still used today for Gethyllis afra, an unusual member of the amaryllis family.

*1 The April fool or blood flower* Haemanthus coccineus *puts on a spectacular autumn display to attract sunbirds and bees. The seeds mature and germinate just in time for winter's first rain showers.*
*2 Increasingly rare on Table Mountain, the succulent* Orbea variegata *was one of the first Cape plants to be described by European botanists. Table Mountain's proximity to a major city means that plants like these are under constant threat from unscrupulous collectors.*

## THE EARLY NATURALISTS

The Cape Peninsula has been occupied by humans for at least 200 000 years. Long before European explorers arrived with their collecting boxes, the first investigations of natural history were made by the hunter-gatherer San or "bushmen", and later by the nomadic Khoi-khoi pastoralists. Motivated by need and expediency rather than scientific curiosity, they learnt about the effects of veld-burning and the food value of plants through trial and error. Some Khoi-khoi plant names like buchu (aromatic plants belonging to the lemon family Rutaceae) and kukumakranka (an amaryllid with edible fruits) are still in use today. The Khoi-khoi had many medicinal uses for Cape plants, some of which were recorded in the journals of explorers like Thunberg and Sparrman.

The accounts of the early explorers at the Cape offer a unique insight into the natural history of Table Mountain. Through their journals, it is possible to picture what the lower slopes of the mountain were like before they were covered by today's urban sprawl. Their writings contain valuable records of species now extinct on Table Mountain, such as vultures and leopards.

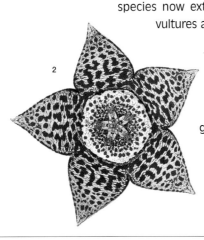

The April fool or blood flower *Haemanthus coccineus* was probably the first plant to be collected from Table Mountain. Blossoming directly out of the ground, its strange red flowers must have immediately evoked interest in the early colonists. An illustration of the blood flower in a publication by the Flemish botanist de L'Obel in 1605 may have been the first appearance of a Cape plant in a European publication.

Justus Huernius, a clergyman who visited the Cape in 1644, made several collections, including the bizarre succulent that was named *Stapelia virgata* (now *Orbea variegata*) by Linnaeus. Linnaeus himself never visited the Cape, although he described hundreds of local species. He maintained regular correspondence with Ryk Tulbagh, one of the early Dutch governors at the Cape, whose name is immortalised in the plant genus *Tulbaghia* and the mountain pride butterfly *Aeropetes tulbaghia*.

But it was the arrival in 1772 of two enthusiastic Swedish naturalists, Carl Thunberg and Anders Sparrman, that put the Cape on the botanical map. Both former pupils of Linnaeus, they wrote valuable accounts of their travels in South Africa, and ever since their visit close botanical links between Sweden and the Cape have been maintained.

Carl Thunberg is rightly known as the father of Cape botany. He collected more than 3 000 specimens in South Africa, 1 000 of which were new to science. Many of these were collected on the slopes of Table Mountain, including the cluster orchid *Disa ferruginea*. Thunberg claimed to have climbed Table Mountain 15 times during his stay at the Cape, usually with a slave to carry his reference books and collecting equipment. He also teamed up with Francis Masson, an English gardener who had been dispatched from Kew, and together they made several forays onto the slopes of the mountain and further afield.

Thunberg was not only a collector, but also made notes on various aspects of natural history. His journal is filled with his observations, as well as accounts of the medicinal uses of indigenous Cape plants. After the death of Linnaeus' son, Thunberg became professor of botany at Uppsala University, and his herbarium there remains the most important reference collection of Cape plants.

Thunberg unexpectedly met up with his old acquaintance Anders Sparrman on his arrival in Cape Town, and the two spent a happy few days collecting together. Later, Sparrman wrote an account of his travels which is a revealing insight into his impressions of the Cape flora. At times he seems disenchanted by the vegetation on Table Mountain – "The bushes and trees (if they may so be called) which here and there grow wild, are stunted partly by their own nature, and partly by the south-east and north-west winds. Hence they, most of them, look dried up, with pale blighted leaves, and upon the whole have a miserable appearance ..." Sparrman's initial interest in botany seemed to wane during his travels in

South Africa, but was soon replaced by a curiosity for animals.

William Burchell, an Englishman who arrived at the Cape in 1810, is more famous for his extensive journeys across South Africa than for botanising at the Cape, but along the way he collected more than 40 000 botanical specimens, including many from the slopes of Table Mountain. Burchell was ahead of his time in recognising the mutual interdependency of plants, a subject that would now be called ecology. "In the wide system of created things, nothing is wanting, nothing is superfluous; the smallest weed or insect is an indispensable necessary to the general good, as the largest object we behold. Each has its peculiar part to perform, conducive ultimately to the well being of all," he wrote. Today, ecologists are not at all sure about the indispensability

of each organism in an ecosystem, but Burchell was a pioneer in transcending the simple zeal of many explorers to collect for the sake of collecting.

Burchell was intrigued by the narrow distributions of many Cape species, such as the silver trees that only occur in a few localised areas on the slopes of Table Mountain. He also discovered that some members of the protea family were dioecious, having male and female flowers on different plants. But his greatest contribution was his recommendation that a botanical garden be established in Cape Town. Unfortunately, he did not live to see his dream materialise 100 years later in the form of the Kirstenbosch Botanical Garden.

Charles Darwin visited the Cape very briefly in June 1836. He had time only to examine certain geological phenomena at Three Anchor Bay before departing on the famous HMS *Beagle*. If only he had been able to climb Table Mountain, perhaps he might have offered an explanation for the diversity of species in the fynbos, a puzzle that still taxes the minds of modern botanists.

No botanist has been more closely associated with Table Mountain than Rudolf Marloth, considered by many to be the founder of modern botany in South Africa. Although he is probably best known as the author of the four-volume *Flora of South Africa* and *Das Kapland*, his monumental German work on the Cape flora, he also wrote numerous scientific papers on aspects of the natural history of the fynbos. It was on Table Mountain that he made the celebrated discovery of how red disas are pollinated by mountain pride butterflies, and took the first measurements of moisture precipitation from the "tablecloth". Marloth is also credited with the first observations of ants dispersing the seeds of fynbos plants.

**3** *Red disas* Disa uniflora *still flourish alongside streams on Table Mountain. In 1895 Rudolf Marloth discovered that the spectacular flowers of this orchid are pollinated by the mountain pride butterfly.*
**4** *Mountain pride butterflies* Aeropetes tulbaghia *pause briefly to drink nectar from the flowers of* Crassula coccinea. *These butterflies play a key role in the ecology of Table Mountain by pollinating at least five plant species with large red flowers.*

1 *Rudolf Marloth used restios like these in a simple experiment to measure moisture precipitation from the "tablecloth".*

Marloth trained as a chemist, and lectured the subject at the Victoria College in Stellenbosch, but he later taught natural sciences, including botany, at the Elsenburg School of Agriculture. His most famous student was Jan Christiaan Smuts, the soldier and politician, who often accompanied Marloth on trips into the mountains to collect plants. His herbarium of more than 20 000 plant specimens is particularly useful to botanists today as a reference for high-altitude species. Marloth was a keen mountaineer and instrumental in the formation of the Mountain Club of South Africa, becoming its second president in 1901. He died in 1931 while botanising in the fynbos, just a few months before the publication of the last volume of his *Flora of South Africa*.

Thomas Stokoe was a neighbour and friend of Marloth's, and they often collected together in the Cape mountains. Stokoe's passion for mountaineering was legendary, and he celebrated his 90th birthday by climbing a peak with Professor Rycroft, then the director of the Kirstenbosch gardens. Stokoe collected some 16 000 specimens, many of

# Jan Smuts

There is a path that winds its way up the forested glades of Skeleton Gorge and through the fynbos to Maclear's Beacon. This was the favourite walking route of Jan Christiaan Smuts, who was reputed to have climbed Table Mountain almost every Sunday when Parliament was meeting in Cape Town. While much is known about his political life, few are aware that he was also an amateur botanist of some repute. A story is told of how a visiting American botanist expressed surprise at his knowledge of grasses, asking how it was that she was "learning all of this not from a professor, but from a general". The famous statesman replied, "My dear lady, I'm only a general in my spare time."

The roots of Smuts' love for nature can be traced to his childhood spent on a farm at Riebeek West, within sight of Table Mountain. But it was only later, through a close friendship with the great Rudolf Marloth, that Smuts developed a keen interest in the scientific aspects of botany. Smuts accompanied Marloth on numerous botanical expeditions into the Cape mountains, and also often teamed up with Thomas Stokoe, the legendary plant collector. Many of the specimens Smuts collected were identified by Harriet Bolus, whose father-in-law Harry Bolus established the Bolus Herbarium,

SA LIBRARY: CAPE TIMES COLLECTION

today housed at the University of Cape Town. Yet he was critical of botanists who never ventured beyond the confines of their laboratories. "Botany is a science of life, and cannot be learned fully from the dead, from dried specimens buried in paper covers. All great botanists have been naturalists, field

naturalists, studying nature from life, wanderers and seekers for the precious secrets, which only intimate contact with the living can disclose," he wrote.

Smuts was fascinated by evolution and the origins of the Cape flora, and he enthusiastically endorsed the now widely accepted idea of ancient land connections between the Cape, Australia, South America and Antarctica. He was also ahead of his time in recognising the great damage caused to the mountain by the planting of alien pine trees. He viewed the pines with disdain, referring to them in a letter to a friend as "these useless horrid pines, the planting of which in the Peninsula has been a calamity".

Smuts lived by the philosophy that human society and the natural world are inseparable. In a speech at the war memorial at Maclear's Beacon, he exhorted a large crowd to find inspiration in the mountains, in order to rise above life's drudgery and despair. "The Mountain is not merely something eternally sublime. It has a great historic and spiritual meaning for us. It stands for us as the ladder of the soul, and in a curious way the source of religion", were his moving words.

Smuts last climbed Table Mountain in 1950, a few months before his death at the age of 80.

them on Table Mountain. No fewer than 30 new plant species were named after him.

Harry Bolus was a wealthy businessman who contributed greatly to our knowledge of the botany of Table Mountain. His work on the orchids of the Cape Peninsula, published in 1882, is still a standard reference, beautifully illustrated by many of his own paintings. Another of Marloth's sometime climbing partners, Bolus was a keen mountaineer and the text of his book was enriched by his encounters with plants in the field. Bolus founded the first Chair of Botany at the University of Cape Town in 1902, and later bequeathed his large herbarium and library to the university, which today is the leading centre for research on the Cape flora.

The *Flora of the Cape Peninsula*, published in 1950, has long been the primary scientific work on the plant life of Table Mountain. It was edited by R.S. Adamson, the Harry Bolus Professor of Botany at the University of Cape Town between 1923 and 1950, and T.M. Salter, an amateur botanist and retired captain in the Royal Navy. Mary Maytham Kidd's *Wildflowers of the Cape Peninsula*, contain-

ing illustrations of more than 800 species, was also published in 1950. This field guide, available in a new edition from the Botanical Society of South Africa, has contributed immeasurably to public awareness of the flora of Table Mountain.

No history of botanical exploration in the Cape would be complete without mention of Elsie Esterhuysen, a botanical hunter-gatherer extraordinaire. An avid mountaineer who specialised in high-altitude Cape flora, she collected more than 36 000 specimens between 1938 and 1990. She has discovered at least 150 new taxa, including a new *Crassula* species that she found while roped to a sheer rock face.

So botanists from Europe and later from South Africa slowly accomplished the massive task of naming the Cape flora. As the twentieth century draws to a close, the rate of discovery of new species has slowed to a trickle. Now the major challenge for botanists is to work out the evolutionary relationships between species and to discover how each contributes to the functioning of the fynbos ecosystem.

**2** *The main body of Table Mountain is a block of hard, cracked sandstone, which sits on a granite pedestal. Sandwiched in between these two is the Graafwater Formation, a thin layer of soft siltstone. In the north the granite is replaced by Malmesbury Shale, which erodes into gentle hills such as Signal Hill and the lower slopes of Devil's Peak.*

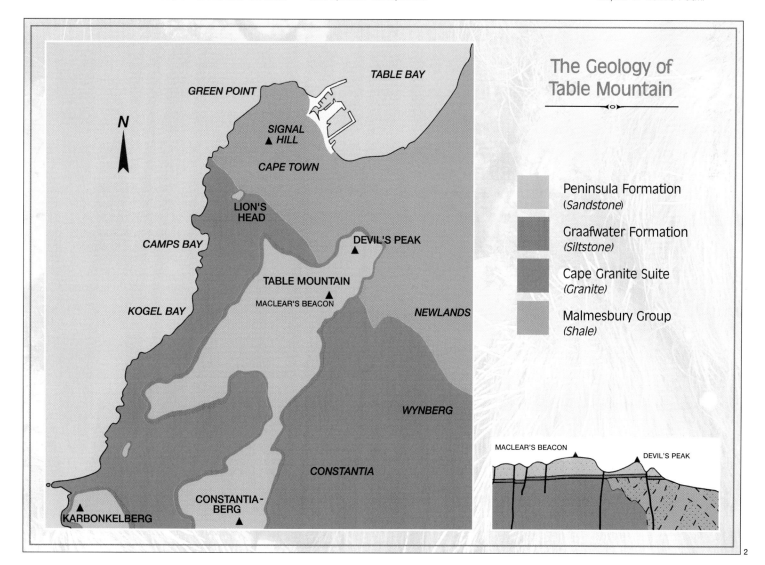

The Geology of Table Mountain

TABLE BAY
GREEN POINT
N
SIGNAL ▲ HILL
CAPE TOWN
LION'S HEAD
CAMPS BAY
DEVIL'S PEAK ▲
TABLE MOUNTAIN
MACLEAR'S BEACON ▲
KOGEL BAY
NEWLANDS
WYNBERG
CONSTANTIA
KARBONKELBERG ▲
CONSTANTIA-BERG ▲

Peninsula Formation (*Sandstone*)

Graafwater Formation (*Siltstone*)

Cape Granite Suite (*Granite*)

Malmesbury Group (*Shale*)

MACLEAR'S BEACON
DEVIL'S PEAK

2

1  *A hollow, eroded into the mountain's soft sandstone by naturally acidic rainwater, holds enough soil and moisture to encourage the growth of shallow-rooted restios and buchu.*
2  *Ripple marks on Lion's Head are evidence of the marine origin of Table Mountain sandstone.*
3  *Chapman's Peak Drive provides an excellent view of the Graafwater Formation.*

## BEGINNINGS

The story of Table Mountain begins long before the flowering plants and dinosaurs appeared. Its history can be traced from the oldest rocks lying at the base of the mountain: soft layers of shales and slates that were deposited more than 600 million years ago as fine silt and clay on the bed of a shallow sea. These ancient shales, known as the Malmesbury Group, are exposed on the lower slopes of Devil's Peak and on Signal Hill, where they have weathered to form a relatively rich clay soil.

Another ancient type of rock found at the base of Table Mountain is granite. Molten magma from deep beneath the earth's crust forced its way through the Malmesbury shales between 1 000 and 500 million years ago, and became granite as it cooled and crystallised. In places, injection of hot molten magma into the Malmesbury shales resulted in rock with a streaky appearance, and it was examples of these rocks at Three Anchor Bay that Charles Darwin examined when the HMS *Beagle* docked in Cape Town in 1836.

The shales and granite were weathered and eroded into a low, flattened landscape 500 million years ago. This subsided beneath the sea to form a shallow basement onto which the soft reddish shales and siltstones of the Graafwater Formation were deposited. Along the Chapman's Peak road the marine legacy of the Graafwater Formation is clearly evident from ripple marks left by wave action on shallow mud flats, and the tracks and burrows of small invertebrates.

The deposition of coarse-grained sand particles which would become the Peninsula Formation began about 450 million years ago, when plant life as we know it was just beginning. On land, the first primitive mosses and ferns had made an appearance. Rivers flowing through this ancient landscape deposited fine sand grains along their banks and on the beaches of the continental shelf, forming a progressively thicker layer as the coastline subsided. On Table Mountain the Peninsula Formation is about 700 metres thick. It is the rock type most important in shaping the mountain's ecology, because soils derived from sandstone are very poor in mineral nutrients, especially phosphorus and nitrogen.

The Cape mountains were formed about 250 million years ago when a small oceanic continent collided with and slid under the southern part of Gondwanaland, the great landmass that once included Africa, Australia, India, Antarctica and South America. The impact caused the Table Mountain Group and other overlaying rocks to become crumpled and folded in places, the rock strata rising thousands of metres in some parts.

Table Mountain appears to have been far from the point of collision, as there is none of the immense folding which can be seen in other Cape mountains. Many of the ravines leading to its summit originated as geological faults, where the rocks split and moved along fault lines. When the continents began to move apart about 140 million years ago, decompression fragmented the sandstone into blocks. At that time the newly formed Cape mountains were probably cloaked with forests of giant ferns and primitive gymnosperms, the forerunners of today's conifers.

After the collision, the more recent Bokkeveld and Witteberg Groups were gradually eroded away, exposing the Table Mountain Group which had been lying compressed under thousands of metres of rock for millions of years. Table Mountain was once continuous with the other Cape mountains, but over the millennia erosion has cleared away the intervening sandstone layers. Some estimates indicate that it was probably twice its present height before erosion took its toll, and that it may be levelled by this ongoing process within the next ten million years.

Africa and South America separated 130 million years ago, resulting in a new coastline for the Cape. The supercontinent of Gondwanaland finally broke apart 120 million years ago, about the same time as the first flowering plants were beginning to establish themselves as serious competitors to the gymnosperms. Some of these prototypes of modern Cape plants were marooned on the continent of Australia as it drifted off towards the east, explaining many of the similarities between the present-day floras of the two regions.

The last two million years have been characterised by a succession of Ice Ages. Many parts of the world, including northern Europe, were under

4

ice sheets that completely obliterated the flora. In the Cape, permanent ice only covered the high mountains, but Table Mountain would have remained exposed because of its relatively low elevation and proximity to the sea. This may be one of the reasons for the large number of plant species on the mountain today, compared to other areas.

During the glaciations so much water was bound up in ice that the sea level dropped by about 100 metres. False Bay would then have been largely dry land, providing an explanation for the remarkably close similarities between the floras of the Cape

**4** *Testimony to an ancient geological drama, the streaky patterns on these rocks at Three Anchor Bay resulted from the fusion of hot magma from the earth's core with the older shales that lie beneath Table Mountain. Charles Darwin visited this site during his famous voyage on the Beagle.*
**5** *About 400 million years ago, when these sandstone rocks were being deposited, giant clubmosses ruled the first forests. Today their descendants are confined to marginal habitats and some, such as this Huperzia gnidioides, have become rock-living specialists, or lithophytes.*
**6** *Rounded by the force of countless waves, granite boulders line most of the Peninsula's northern shores.*

5

6

Peninsula and Cape Hangklip on each side of the bay. During the warmer interglacial periods the polar ice caps partially melted, causing the sea level to rise above its present levels. The Cape Flats were then probably covered in sea water, with Table Mountain an island about 30 kilometres from the mainland.

## MOISTURE FROM THE TABLECLOTH

Table Mountain's famous "tablecloth" is a spectacular sight, appearing when moist air rises over the back of the mountain and condenses in the cool air of the summit. Wisps of cloud stream over the precipices, only to dissipate in the warm air rising from below.

The tablecloth is most common in summer, when the prevailing south-easterly wind buffets the mountain. While the lower slopes bake in the relentless heat and drought of summer, the upper slopes are enshrouded in a cool and moist blanket of cloud. Droplets of moisture cling to plants, and if the tablecloth persists for long enough the ground becomes wet and swampy. There is even a small lake near Maclear's Beacon that is occasionally filled in summer by moisture precipitated from the tablecloth.

The first person to suggest that the summit plateau received water from clouds was the botanical explorer Carl Thunberg, who in 1772 noted that the clouds "diffuse themselves over the mountain without falling down below in rain". But the true importance of the tablecloth was not realised until the beginning of this century, when naturalist Rudolf Marloth set out to prove that the lush vegetation on the summit plateau was due to condensation. Marloth believed that the leaves of plants capture water from clouds, and to test his theory he carried out a series of ingenious and elegant experiments. His method was to compare the water caught by a standard rain gauge with one he had modified by inserting a bunch of restios into the funnel. The results were astonishing: the gauge with restios caught 20 times more water than the standard one.

After its publication in 1904, Marloth's work was met with scepticism from scientists, but he carefully repeated the experiments and reconfirmed his earlier findings in a 1907 publication. Today Marloth's findings are generally accepted and his pioneering technique for measuring fog precipitation has been adapted for a wide range of uses. The Weather Bureau has estimated the fog precipitation on the summit of Table Mountain during one year to be 3 294 millimetres, nearly double the precipitation from rainfall.

**1** *Discovered only in 1997, this small orchid is known from just five individuals. It has been named* Disa nubigena, *the disa "grown from the cloud", as it occurs only on the summit of Devil's Peak, where moisture from the tablecloth allows it to flower in the drought of summer.*
**2** *The front face of Table Mountain, shrouded by the famous tablecloth, forms a spectacular backdrop to the brilliant red flowers of the Guernsey lily* Nerine sarniensis, *which bloomed on Lion's Head after a fire swept the area in the summer of 1996.*

Botanists now believe that plants on the summit of Table Mountain are spared from the annual drought of summer by precipitation from the table-cloth. The phenomenon almost certainly explains the uniqueness of the vegetation of the summit plateau, and the presence of moisture-loving plants like *Disa longicornu*, *Disa uniflora* and *Anemone tenuifolia*, which are found only on the mountain's higher slopes.

Capetonians know that the south-easter does not always result in the formation of a tablecloth. On some days the wind howls fiercely through the city and the mountain has not a trace of cloud. This is because an inversion layer of descending air below the height of Table Mountain "caps" the south-easter, preventing it from passing over the mountain and forming the tablecloth.

### WINTER RAINFALL

The climate at the Cape changed dramatically with the break-up of Gondwanaland. Low-pressure cells associated with rain-bearing frontal systems began sweeping eastward across the South Atlantic. Today, a high-pressure cell located off the coast of South Africa during summer prevents these frontal systems from passing over the Cape, but during winter the cell weakens and the frontal systems deposit rain on the Cape as they move towards the equator. This seasonal oscillation began about three million years ago and resulted in our present-day mediterranean-type climate of dry summers and wet winters.

The arrival of a rain-bearing cold front is heralded by a stream of high cirrus clouds in the upper atmosphere, followed by a menacing north-westerly wind. Heavy cloud hangs over the mountain and

*1 Raindrops dangle from restio stalks after a winter rain shower. Winter rather than summer rainfall sets the Cape apart from the rest of Africa, allowing its flora to evolve in isolation from plants further north, which are adapted to a warm and wet summer growing season.*
*2 An island mountain, Lion's Head drifts in a sea of mist brought in from the cold Atlantic by mild south-westerly breezes – weather typical of autumn and spring.*

the rain seems interminable. Temporary waterfalls cascade down the slopes as the water flows off the front table.

A geographer's rule-of-thumb is that most rain falls on the side of a mountain which faces the prevailing wind, but this does not apply on Table Mountain. Here the highest rainfall figures (nearly 2 000 millimetres per annum) are recorded from Newlands on the leeward, eastern slopes of Table Mountain, while Camps Bay on the windward side receives less than 600 millimetres. The reason for this paradox is that Table Mountain is not high enough to prevent the north-westerly wind from passing over the mountain, so sodden air rises to the summit, condenses, and falls as rain on the opposite side. During a winter storm the turbulence caused by wind rushing over the edge of Table Mountain can result in freak gales, which uproot trees and tear the roofs off houses.

in autumn, when moist air moving over the Atlantic condenses as it meets the cold Benguela Current on the west coast. At such times Table Mountain appears to be floating in a sea of cloud as the fog envelops the lower reaches of the mountain.

These seasonal changes have important implications for the life cycles of Cape plants. For example, the belladonna or March lily *Amaryllis belladonna* has fleshy seeds which cannot withstand extended periods of dryness, so the seeds are produced just in time for the first rains of winter. The life cycles of many animals are also timed according to the winter rains.

The advent of a mediterranean climate at the Cape about three million years ago would have had major effects on the vegetation. The humid forests would have retreated, while the shrubby Cape flora probably expanded its range. Dry summer conditions would also have increased the incidence of fires. Around this time, many Cape plants evolved special properties to allow them to survive fire. It is fire, more than any other factor, that has shaped the fynbos.

3

*3 The northern and western faces of Table Mountain receive substantially less rain than the eastern and southern slopes, where the annual precipitation is almost 2 metres.*
*4 Under a chilly cover of mist, residents of Camps Bay at the foot of the Twelve Apostles would never guess that the rest of Cape Town had clear skies. By channelling and blocking winds and clouds, Table Mountain has a dramatic influence on the city's climate.*

After the front has passed, the winds shift direction; cold air usually streams in from the southern Atlantic and temperatures may drop below freezing. Snowfalls on Table Mountain are infrequent, but during the winter of 1995 a thick blanket of snow covered the upper slopes for two days.

Cold fronts are sometimes preceded by a "berg" wind, which is a hot, dry wind blowing from the interior region. The rise in temperature during a berg wind can be astonishing: during a winter morning in 1985, the temperature in Cape Town rose from 3 °C at 07:00 to 27 °C at 07:35.

Lightning is rare in the Western Cape, usually occurring only a few times per year, and mostly during autumn when cut-off low-pressure systems result in thunderstorms. Lightning strikes during a thunderstorm in Easter 1991 set off fynbos wildfires in many parts of the Western Cape.

The highest incidence of coastal fog also occurs

4

# The Power of Fire

I t is the end of summer, and the slopes of Lion's Head are a mosaic of olive-greens and browns, splashed with a haze of flowering pink ericas. Sugarbirds dart between the king proteas, and nearby an orangebreasted sunbird weaves through an erica bush. On a lichen-blotched boulder, a male agama bobs his blue head challengingly. All but a few of the streams on the mountain have run dry and the fynbos crackles underfoot.

The tranquillity is deceptive, however, for the fynbos is a tinderbox at this time of year, and the smallest flame can spark an inferno. Fanned by the summer south-easter, it will sweep across this landscape in an instant, devouring everything in its path.

Fynbos is very conducive to the spread of fires, not only because the finely branched plants are an effective kindling, but also because they tend to accumulate dead plant material in their canopies, rather than shedding it. The combustion of this material drives out what little water is in the living leaves, which then ignite and add to the conflagration. Some fynbos plants, such as buchus, also contain oils in their leaves, rendering them highly flammable.

Natural fires are usually caused by lightning, but on the Cape Peninsula, where thunderstorms are uncommon, almost all fires are started by people, either inadvertently or as part of a management plan. In 1996 a fire on Lion's Head spread from the temporary shelter of some "bergies" – vagrants who live on the slopes of the mountain. Whipped up by the south-easterly wind, the fire raged all night, engaged in a deadly duel with scores of firefighters. The morning newspapers captured the drama of the night: the city had been saved, but the mountain seemed devastated.

*OPPOSITE: Flowers of flame – inside the protective flowerheads, the seeds of the king protea Protea cynaroides will be safe from the scorching flames.*
*1 Fire licks at the cones of a protea.*
*2 A fire leaves apparent devastation in its wake, but with the first rains of winter, new life will emerge with vigour.*

*1 Smoke clears to reveal an altered landscape. Most of the fynbos plants have been killed by the flames, but chemicals in the smoke will trigger the germination of hidden seeds.*
*2 Angulate tortoises* Chersina angulata *are among the victims of a rare fire in strandveld.*
*3 By hiding under a rock, two ocellated geckoes* Pachydactylus geitje *escaped the flames.*
*4 With only slightly singed fur, a vlei rat* Otomys irroratus *is a lucky survivor. It will soon be feasting on newly released protea seeds.*
*5 Very little is known about the effect of fire on insects. Presumably many winged insects, such as this praying mantis, survive, while species with subterranean larvae or pupae might actually be stimulated to hatch.*
*6 Fires are unnaturally frequent in areas adjacent to the city, such as Lion's Head. The extinction from these areas of species such as the pincushion* Leucospermum vestitum *and the velvet worm* Peripatopsis leonina *is believed to be attributable to overly frequent fires.*

## THE DAY AFTER

The fire transformed the Lion's Head landscape. In the immediate aftermath, black skeletons of protea bushes still smouldered, and a layer of soft, warm ash covered the ground. Underneath a blackened boulder, two ocellated geckoes *Pachydactylus geitje* shared a refuge, while other rocks sheltered ant nests and baboon spiders. Many insects had been killed by the flames, but others had escaped by flying away or had endured as pupae, eggs and larvae hidden underground.

Some insects are even able to survive fire by sheltering inside ant nests, while parrot-beaked tortoises *Homopus areolatus* take refuge deep inside rodent burrows. The larger angulate tortoises *Chersina angulata* are less adept at escaping fires, which may explain why they are more common in the relatively inflammable strandveld. Tortoises bury their eggs approximately 5 centimetres below the soil, and these will usually survive low-intensity fires.

Rodents can also find refuge under rocks or in burrows, although species with above-ground nests, such as vlei rats *Otomys irroratus*, are less fortunate. Nevertheless, the rodents that do survive find themselves in a totally altered habitat with little vegetation for either food or shelter. The sharp drop in rodent numbers immediately after a fire therefore reflects the combined effects of emigration, death by fire and predation, the population typically taking about a year to recover. The species composition may also change during this period; for example, the diurnal striped mouse *Rhabdomys pumilio*, which forages under the cover of dense bushes to escape detection by aerial predators, disappears after fire, while the pigmy mouse *Mus minutoides* can tolerate open environments and so its numbers increase.

Despite the bleakness of the landscape in the wake of a fire, life is already preparing to re-emerge with new vigour. The proteas and leucadendrons are among the first to stir, their singed seed cones creaking open in response to the fire's desiccating influence. The top-shaped cones of the tolbos *Leucadendron rubrum* are the quickest

**1** A sugarbush Protea repens *with a good crop of mature cones goes up in flames. The death of the parent plant and the desiccating effect of the fire cause the cones' scales to open, spilling their tufted seeds into the wind (**2**). The cones of* Leucadendron rubrum *are much quicker to respond, and open within minutes of a fire's passing (**3**). Seeds that germinate in the rich ash of a burnt land-scape (**4**) have the benefit of increased nutrients, reduced predation and less competition from adult plants.*

to react, and the seeds are already fluffing out between the parting scales within an hour or two of the fire's passing. Responding more slowly, the cones of the silver tree *Leucadendron argenteum* release large black nuts that parachute down to the ground and then tumble along until their journey is halted by some obstacle. The fluffy, golden seeds of the common sugarbush *Protea repens* bounce along the ground in a similar manner, and typically collect in drifts around the bases of charred bushes.

The seeds released from a protea bush are not only the product of the previous year's flowering, but rather the yield that has accumulated over many years. The plant releases few, if any, seeds during its lifetime and instead stores them in anticipation of fire. Besides proteas, several other species store their seeds in fireproof cones, including the mountain cypress *Widdringtonia nodiflora*, which has circular, resinous cones borne in sequential clusters around the stem. One cypress can have up to five clusters of closed cones along its stem, representing five years of seed production. When a fire kills the stem, the segments of the cone part to release the winged seeds.

Why do plants wait for a fire to release their seeds? For a start, seeds that are released into a burnt landscape are less likely to be eaten by rodents, as the few that remain will soon be glutted by the over-abundance of seeds, leaving the vast majority untouched. Once they have germinated the seedlings too will benefit from the scarcity of grazing rodents. But the main advantage for seedlings is the destruction of the domineering community of adult plants and the release of their nutrients in a rich bed of ash. The burnt landscape is so conducive to seed and seedling survival that almost all fynbos plants have adopted some form of fire-stimulated reproduction. In fact, it is almost impossible to find seedlings in fynbos at any time other than immediately after a fire.

Having survived the fire and their journey from the parent plant, the fate of the seeds now depends on the vagaries of the weather. Many fynbos seeds need not only rain, but also the cold conditions of winter to germinate. Autumn fires are ideal because winter is not far behind, but fires in spring or early summer can be disastrous because the seeds will be exposed to seed-eaters and the scorching summer sun for months. In this respect, small burns, which are more easily recolonised by seed-eaters, may have more serious consequences than large ones, while successive spring fires may cause the local extinction of species with canopy-stored seeds.

## THE FIRST RAIN OF WINTER

One month after the fire on Lion's Head, the burnt slopes appeared little changed at first glance, but closer inspection revealed clusters of new green shoots pushing up through the soil. Around the base of a charred taaibos *Rhus lucida*, delicately unfurling leaves were sprouting from its subterranean tuber, which had been protected from the fire by an insulating layer of soil.

Nearby, new life was also sprouting from the blackened trunk of a waboom *Protea nitida*. The thick bark of the waboom serves as a fireproof armour, protecting the green buds underneath from heat damage. Although the silver tree *Leucadendron argenteum*, the pincushion *Leucospermum conocarpodendron* and the Peninsula-endemic *Mimetes fimbriifolius* also have thick, protective bark, they lack the buds beneath it, and are able to survive only mild fires by sprouting from buds in the canopy that remain unscorched after the flames have passed.

Like the taaibos, bulbous plants such as watsonias and chincherinchees have underground food stores and produce new leaves at the onset of winter from buds protected below the soil, while grasses and restios resprout from underground runners. All of these plants are "sprouters", able to survive fire by sprouting from buds that are protected by a thick bark or layer of soil.

Apart from the green shoots of the sprouters, there is also a sprinkling of emerging seedlings. Most of these are "non-sprouters" – species that are killed by fire and depend entirely on seed for regeneration. Since they need make no investment in fire-surviving devices such as thick bark and underground food stores, non-sprouters are free to put all their resources into the production of seeds. The seedlings of non-sprouters not only outnumber those of sprouters, but also grow more quickly, with the result that they are likely to win any competition for space. This fact alone may explain why fynbos landscapes are dominated by plants that are killed by fire.

5 *Not all plants are killed by fire; many, such as this cock's comb fern* Schizaea pectinata, *survive as adult plants and then sprout new growth from their protected buds.*
6 Mimetes fimbriifolius *can survive mild fires by virtue of its thick bark, and sprouts again from buds high in the canopy.*
7 *Very hot fires will kill adult pincushions* Leucospermum conocarpodendron, *but stimulate their seeds, buried deep inside ant nests, to germinate.*

# Ant treasure troves

About 20 per cent of the fynbos plants on the Cape Peninsula enlist ants to disperse their seeds, a strategy known as myrmecochory. The ants carry the seeds into their underground chambers, where they are safe from rodents and other seed predators, as well as the scorching heat of fires.

The ants harvest the seeds for their attached food bodies, called elaiosomes. In most species, such as *Mimetes fimbriifolius* and the restio *Hypodiscus aristatus*, the food body is an obvious pale knob on one end of the seed, but in pincushions the entire seed is coated in a white, nutrient-rich layer. Unlike most fleshy fruits, the food bodies on ant-dispersed seeds are small and relatively inexpensive to produce, so they are an ideal option for nutrient-limited fynbos plants. Once the seed is underground, the ants devour the food body. Some seeds are then ejected from the nest, but most remain underground.

Many ant-dispersed species release their seeds in midsummer, at the height of ant activity, ensuring that the seeds are discovered within minutes. The diligence with which ants transport seeds suggests that there might be more involved than just a food reward. Indeed, the scents produced by some food bodies are similar to the pheromones that ants use in communication, so it is quite possible that the ants are fooled into believing that the seeds are ant larvae, or dead ants, that need to be carried into the nest.

*Dragged by an energetic workforce of* Anoplolepis *ants, a seed of the pincushion tree* Leucospermum conocarpodendron *is about to disappear into an underground labyrinth. There it will lie dormant until the heat and smoke of a fire raging above ground stimulate its germination.*

Remarkably, several insects play the same game. The hard, seed-like eggs of stick insects, which have what appears to be a food body attached to one end, are also taken into ant nests, where they are safe from fires and parasitic wasps. Furthermore, many of the small butterflies on Table Mountain spend their larval stages inside ant nests, as discussed in the chapter "Hunting and Hiding".

Ant dispersal is not a uniquely fynbos phenomenon. The south-western region of Australia also has many ant-dispersed plants, and some of these, such as the invasive Port Jackson willow *Acacia saligna*, have been introduced to the Cape and are now dispersed by local ants.

The most important seed dispersers in the fynbos are the pugnacious ants *Anoplolepis*, which feed primarily on other insects. They live together in large colonies with multi-entrance nests in the open areas between bushes. This is advantageous for seeds dispersed by ants, as they avoid competition with the wind-dispersed seeds of many species of *Protea*, which after a fire tend to collect around the base of bushes. Cocktail ants *Crematogaster* are active in the canopies of bushes, where they interfere with dispersal by removing the food bodies from seeds before they have dropped to the ground. Fortunately, cocktail ants prefer strandveld, and are not as common in fynbos because their elevated paper nests are vulnerable to fires.

Although ants are good at burying seeds, they are not very good at transporting them over long distances. Seeds are typically carried only a few metres to the nearest nest entrance, so there is little mixing among populations of ant-dispersed plants. This increases the likelihood that different populations of a species will diverge from each other over time and become separate species. In this way, ant dispersal may be partly responsible for both the explosion of plant diversity at the Cape and the prevalence of endemic species on the Peninsula.

Introduced Argentine ants *Linepithema humile* have displaced local ants from many areas of the Cape Peninsula, with alarming consequences. These aliens devour the food bodies, but do not bury the seeds, leaving them at the mercy of fire and rodents.

Even in unburnt fynbos landscapes, plants with these two different life-history strategies can be distinguished from each other. The sprouters, such as the king protea *Protea cynaroides*, usually have multiple stems emanating from a swollen underground trunk. Since they survive fire as adults, a range of plants of various ages can be found in any one area, including some very old plants that have survived several fires. Non-sprouters, like the blackbeard sugarbush *Protea lepidocarpodendron*, are single-stemmed and form stands comprising a single age-class, as all the plants germinated together after a fire.

Many of the seedlings that emerge in the fire-ravaged landscape belong to species such as *Erica baccans* and *Mimetes hirtus*, which do not have cones in their canopies. Instead of releasing seeds en masse after a fire they release small quantities throughout their lifetime, allowing a stockpile of seeds to accumulate in the soil, where they lie dormant until a fire passes overhead. Some species accelerate the burial process by enticing ants to carry the seeds into their underground nests.

Only the heat of an intense fire roaring overhead will break the dormancy of some large and deeply buried seeds, such as those of *Leucospermum conocarpodendron* and *Mimetes fimbriifolius*. In these hard-seeded species, the heat dries out the seed coat to such an extent that subsequent wetting causes it to crack, allowing water to enter the seed and awaken the embryo inside from its dormant state. Legumes such as *Aspalathus* and the keurboom *Virgilia oroboides* have a special weak spot in the seed coat that ruptures in the heat of the fire and allows the entry of water.

Many smaller-seeded fynbos plants, such as the Peninsula-endemic false heath *Audouinia capitata*, need only smoke to initiate germination. How this is achieved is unclear, although nitrogen dioxide in the smoke is one possible trigger. Finally, there are seeds that respond to fire-induced habitat alteration. The removal of vegetation cover causes soil temperatures to rise dramatically during the day and plummet at night, and these temperature fluctuations are the germination cue for some species.

The intensity of a fire also determines which species will germinate. Seeds found in the upper layers of soil, such as those of slangbos *Stoebe plumosa*, are killed by very intense fires, while mild fires might not provide sufficient stimulus to initiate germination in deeply buried seeds, as in pincushions, or very hard seeds, as in legumes.

Fires differ in intensity according to the size of the fuel load, the speed at which the fire-front moves, and weather conditions. Fires in old, dense veld are hotter than grass fires in young veld. Similarly, fires on warm, dry and windy afternoons are hotter than those on cool, calm mornings. Backfires, which burn downhill or against the wind, spread slowly and release energy close to the ground, whereas headfires, which burn uphill or with the wind, move faster and release heat in the canopy. There is even variation within one fire, with denser areas, for example, burning hotter than sparse areas. Such variations favour different species in the landscape, and may help to maintain the diversity of species.

Fire-stimulated seed release and germination are two ways of synchronising reproduction with fire, but there is a third way, which is far more spectacular. In April, several weeks after the fire on Lion's Head, various members of the amaryllis family burst into flower for the first time in many years. The swollen flowerheads of the blood flower or April fool *Haemanthus sanguineus* were the first to appear, erupting directly from the earth like red fists in a show of defiance.

The April fool and many other amaryllids flower before they grow leaves, using food stored in the bulb to produce first the flowerhead, and later the

*1 Fire lilies* Cyrtanthus ventricosus *and the leaves of* Watsonia *plants make their appearance within days of a fire.*
*2 Rising phoenix-like from the ashes, blood flowers* Haemanthus sanguineus *add colour and life to a blackened landscape on the slopes of Lion's Head.*

**1** *March lilies* Amaryllis belladonna *erupt from the scorched earth. Their garnet-like seeds germinate soon after being released* (**2**).

**3** *Appearing only after fire, the flowerhead of* Crossyne guttata *dries out when the seeds are mature and breaks off to become a giant tumbleweed, scattering its seeds as it rolls over the ground.*

2

1

3

the spires. The flowers of *Watsonia meriana* were the earliest to appear, each a tubular, salmon-coloured trumpet adapted for bird pollination. One of the varieties of this species, which occurs on Lion's Head, has the unusual characteristic of producing small bulbs on the flower-stalk instead of seeds. These drop off and produce new plants, which are genetically identical to the parent as they are not the result of sexual reproduction.

Soon after the first flowers of *Watsonia meriana* had wilted, the buds of *Watsonia borbonica* began to explode in flashes of pink amid the green foliage. A week later, the west-facing slope of Lion's Head was a solid mass of chest-high flowers. So grand was the floral display that it was clearly visible from Camps Bay beach! It was only a month later that the same species started to bloom on the shaded south-east facing slopes.

That spring, many bulbs were flowering on Lion's Head at the same time as the watsonias. Other flowers of the iris family included the small pink *Ixia scillaris*, the large, pale blue *Aristea spiralis*, the

fleshy red seeds. When the seeds are mature, the flowerhead topples over, and the spilt seeds begin germinating immediately in the rich ash. Since the April fool always flowers in autumn, seed release and germination coincide with the first winter rains.

Not far from the April fools, an acre of March lilies *Amaryllis belladonna* graced the slope, filling the warm evening air with their lemony fragrance. The massive flowers, the largest on the mountain, are borne in bunches on tall, leafless stalks soaring from the bare soil. When the March lilies had finished flowering, the ground was littered with their garnet-like seeds. Within a week, tiny green roots were fingering their way out of the seeds in search of soil. Only then was it time for the leaves to emerge from the bulb.

Other bulbous plants, such as members of the iris, lily and orchid families, also put out their leaves after the first autumn showers. Most of these species flower in spring, but many had not done so for years because dense bushes had crowded them out. Now their bulbs were burgeoning with sufficient starch to fuel the mass production of flowers and seeds, promising a spectacular spring show.

### THE FIRST SPRING

By late winter, the slopes of Lion's Head were bristling with the broad, sword-shaped leaves of watsonias, members of the iris family. As the days lengthened, they started to send up tall spires bedecked with buds, which swelled a little each day until finally the first ones popped at the bottom of

4

lanky yellow *Bobartia indica*, and the locally rare *Lapeirousia corymbosa*. The chincherinchees *Ornithogalum thyrsoides* were the most prominent members of the lily family.

The autumn fire on Lion's Head had been very favourable for bulbous plants, coming at a time when their leaves had dried out and their resources were stored underground. Fires in spring or early summer are less favourable as they destroy green leaves at considerable cost to the plant. Watsonias, for example, bloom very poorly after spring burns.

Fires often reveal rare bulbous plants that have lain dormant for many years and are seen in flower only in the first spring after a fire. This is particularly true of orchids, as their bulbs do not flower until a fire removes the dense vegetation shading them. Although the fire on Lion's Head did not turn up any rare orchids, the profusion of moederkappies *Pterygodium catholicum* helped make up for this. If these small orchids had flowered when they were dwarfed by the surrounding bushes they would have gone unnoticed by their pollinators, but in the burnt landscape they were clearly visible.

Some shrubs also begin to flower soon after fire. Like the bulbs, they are sprouters that make a quick comeback. On Lion's Head the most striking were the pink flowers of the hooded-leafed pelargonium *Pelargonium cucullatum tabulare* and the blue flowers of the wild sage *Salvia africana-caerulea*.

Yet another group of plants grow so rapidly from seeds in the soil that they are able to flower in their first spring, when the seedlings of other plants are still becoming established. Some, such as *Nemesia* and *Hemimeris*, are annuals that die after they have flowered and produced seeds. Others such as *Aspalathus*, *Senecio*, *Roella* and *Helichrysum* may last for two or three years. These plants are called fireweeds, because they grow and flower prolifically only in the first few years after a fire, when vegetation cover is sparse and nutrients are abundant. As the vegetation recovers they disappear from the landscape, but survive as seeds in the soil until the next fire.

**4** *In the first spring after a fire on Lion's Head,* Watsonia borbonica *flowered en masse.*

**5** *The giant flowers of* Homeria ochroleuca *are insect-attracting beacons in the stark, recently burnt landscape.*

5

*Delicate orchids, such as these moederkappies Pterygodium catholicum (1), the bizarre and seldom-seen Pachites bodkinii (2), and the rare spider orchid Bartholina burmanniana (3), normally only flower after a fire has cleared away the dominant shrubs. In a burnt landscape they have a better chance of attracting their specialist pollinators.*

The result of all this spring flowering is that even more seeds are released into the newly burnt landscape, and their seedlings too will benefit from the availability of nutrients and space, and the scarcity of herbivores. As with synchronised seed release by proteas, mass flowering after fires satiates seed predators. For example, when only a few *Watsonia borbonica* plants flower together, they suffer devastating seed predation by snout-nosed weevils,

but only a small percentage of the seeds are damaged when the watsonias flower en masse.

Of course, beautiful though they may be, the charms of flowers are not intended for human appreciation, but solely for the attraction of pollinators. In this respect mass displays have advantages, because they attract larger numbers of pollinators than small groups of flowers. Many pollinators, including the oil-collecting bees that pollinate the flowers of the moederkappies, as well as most butterflies and flies, have larvae that live or pupate underground or beneath rocks. It is even possible that some flower-visiting species might have a pupal or egg stage that can lie dormant in the soil until stimulated to hatch by a fire passing overhead.

Carpenter bees, which nest in the branches of trees and do not have an underground stage, have to recolonise burnt landscapes as winged adults. In the spring after the fire on Lion's Head, the carpenter bees returned in full force. The soft wood of dead silver tree stumps was soon riddled with their tunnels, which were rapidly being filled with a rich harvest of pollen and nectar.

By November, the spring extravaganza on Lion's Head was starting to peter out. The dry summer months that lay ahead would be a long ordeal for the seedlings of the slower-growing species, such as members of the protea and erica families, the number to survive depending largely on the weather. Where clumps of seeds accumulated,

The fire heath Erica cerinthoides (**4**) survives fires and soon sprouts new shoots and flowers from a swollen underground stem. Other ericas that regenerate only from seed take much longer to flower for the first time.

As the veld matures, different plants reach maturity and come into flower. Daisies Ursinia paleacea (**5**) flower in profusion in the second and third year after a fire, while most proteas, such as the green sugarbush Protea coronata (**6**), begin flowering only when the veld is about five years old.

competition among seedlings would also cause many to die, while herbivorous animals would seal the fate of others. In the end, those that would live to see the next fire would be better suited to the demanding conditions of fynbos life.

## THE CHANGING KALEIDOSCOPE

Over the next 15 years, the veld on Lion's Head will grow taller and denser. Many of the plants that flowered in the year after the fire will not do so again, although some, such as the amaryllids and watsonias, might continue to produce leaves on a yearly basis. The fireweeds have disappeared without a trace and now exist only as seeds in the soil. As the years roll by, other plants will flower as they mature, with the result that no spring will be quite like the one before.

The sprouters, especially some of the restios, tend to dominate most fynbos landscapes for the first three or four years after a fire. During this period the non-sprouters are still becoming established as seedlings. Most erica seedlings grow slowly, the rate depending on their ability to strike up mutualistic relationships with soil fungi, which supply the young plants with nutrients. In contrast, members of the pea family typically grow rapidly, because they are able to obtain nutrients by extracting nitrogen directly from the air. Two years after the fire on Lion's Head, for example, the spiny *Aspalathus* had formed an impenetrable thicket

on the moister slopes. Its yellow flowers provided a new splash of colour, and an abundance of food for carpenter bees.

After three or four years, most of the non-sprouting proteas and ericas are still in their juvenile stage, and have not yet produced flowers. This is a very vulnerable period for them. Should a fire sweep across the slope now, it

would kill the saplings, and no seed store would exist to replace them. One untimely fire could cause the immediate extinction of a non-sprouting species that is still in its juvenile phase.

About five years after a fire, most of the non-sprouting proteas and ericas are nearing the end of their juvenile phase, and flower for the first time. Soon, they will have their first seed crop stashed away in cones, or in the soil. From now on their seed store will swell every year in anticipation of the coming fire. If all goes well, the fire will arrive when the proteas and other non-sprouters are about 15 years old. By then they would have flowered ten times, and would have accumulated more than enough seed to replace themselves when they are killed by fire.

The interval between fires is partly determined by the growth rate of plants. As veld matures it accumulates dead material, increasing the chance of successful ignition. In areas of renosterveld, such as Signal Hill and the lower slopes of Devil's Peak, the natural frequency of fires is probably higher than for fynbos areas. Here the richer shale- and granite-derived soils allow for the rapid growth of grasses, and can result in sufficient build-up of fuel within two or three years.

It is unusual for fynbos veld to last more than 20 years before fire resets the clock, but if it does, some interesting changes start to occur. After 30 years some members of the protea family start to show signs of senescence. The branches of large protea bushes, for example, break under their own weight. Although old veld is rare on Table Mountain, senescent proteas in various stages of degradation can be found below the firebreak in Orange Kloof, an area from which fire has been excluded for many years. Gardeners find to their disappointment that planted proteas meet the same fate; instead of becoming massive, ancient bushes, they fall to pieces in their old age.

The problem seems to lie not so much in the quality of the wood of these plants, but rather in the architecture of the bush. Many members of the protea family produce flowers and cones on the tips of their branches, so they branch repeatedly to increase the number that can be carried on the bush. Under most circumstances this is a good strategy, but when the flames stay away for too long the bush becomes disproportionately wide and starts to split at the base.

*A few years after the fire, members of the protea family, such as the sprouting Mimetes hirtus (1), begin to flower, and a recognisable fynbos community of restios, ericas and proteas becomes re-established (2, 3). However, tree-like proteas such as the pincushion Leucospermum conocarpodendron (4) will take many years to reach maturity.*

Old age also takes its toll on seed supplies. The oldest cones on some proteas, such as the black-beard sugarbushes *Protea lepidocarpodendron* and the golden conebush *Leucadendron laureolum*, eventually abandon their wait for fire and open spontaneously, but in an unburnt landscape the seeds have a slim chance of survival. Soil-stored seeds, such as those of the pincushions and mimetes, are also lost after very long fire-free periods. Once plants have become too old to produce more seeds, the number of seeds that are stored in the soil starts to decline and might reach dangerously low levels.

## FORESTS AND FIRE

Some plants thrive in very old veld, where they owe their presence to birds. As the fynbos vegetation becomes denser and taller, it becomes more attractive to forest birds like the sombre bulbul and olive thrush, which bring with them the seeds of forest and thicket plants. The vegetation of forests and coastal thicket (also called strandveld) is not particularly flammable, the plants having large shiny leaves and thick stems. Since these vegetation types are not fire-adapted, strandveld is restricted to the coast, where the sea acts as a buffer from fire, while forest is confined to fire-protected valleys and scree slopes.

Some of the most important differences between fynbos and these vegetation types lie in their seed and seedling biology. Fynbos seeds are either released en masse immediately after a fire and are dispersed by wind, or they are released in between fires and find their way into the soil by various means. Typically they enter a state of dormancy once mature, and germinate only in a bare, burnt landscape. Given this set of circumstances, it would make little sense for fynbos plants to rely on bird dispersal, so fleshy fruits and fruit-eating birds are rare in fynbos. The lack of nutrients in the fynbos landscape probably also limits fruit production.

The seeds of forest and strandveld plants, on the other hand, do not enter a prolonged state of dormancy, but rather germinate soon after maturity, the seedlings becoming established in the intervals between fires. The plants must ensure that their seeds are dispersed to the few sites that are suitable for seedling establishment, so they produce fleshy fruits and enlist the services of fruit-eating animals. In old fynbos, seedlings of forest plants are usually found growing under the tallest proteas, because these provide convenient perches for visiting forest birds.

Prior to the fire on Lion's Head, several forest trees had established a footing in the old silver tree

*1 Two to three decades after a fire, tall fynbos plants such as the silver tree* Leucadendron argenteum *and forest pioneers such as the keurtjie* Podalyria calyptrata *dominate the vegetation.*

1

**2** *On drier slopes, such as those of Little Lion's Head, the camphor bush* Tarchonanthus camphoratus *is among the forest pioneers.*
**3** *In rocky areas and deep ravines, where fire is excluded for long periods, patches of forest trees eventually become established. Fire constantly knocks back the expanding forest and establishes a sharp border between it and the surrounding fynbos.*

stand inside the firebreak, the most abundant being the wild peach *Kiggelaria africana*. A forest pioneer, its seedlings thrive in the relatively sunny conditions of the fynbos. Other forest pioneers include the wild olive *Olea europea africana*, the keurboom *Virgilia oroboides*, klipkershout *Maytenus oleoides*, the common spike-thorn *Gymnosporia buxifolia* and the camphor bush *Tarchonanthus camphoratus*.

The future of the new forest arrivals is at the mercy of fire. If the flames sweep the slope while the forest trees are still small, they will be killed outright, but if given the chance to grow large enough they will be able to survive the fire by sprouting new branches from protected buds. Seedlings need less time to grow into resilient trees on wet, nutrient-rich soils like those derived from granite and shale. Areas with natural fire protection, such as rocky scree slopes and deep, wet valleys, or those protected by a firebreak, such as Orange Kloof, are also likely to be successfully colonised by forest trees.

If fire stays away for long enough, the pioneer trees eventually emerge above the old fynbos plants, creating a micro-climate beneath them that is very different from the sunny habitat in which they themselves germinated. Conditions are no longer conducive to the growth of their own

seedlings, but now a variety of other species are growing up in their shade. These are the seedlings of forest specialists such as the hard pear *Olinia ventosa*, stinkwood *Ocotea bullata* and yellowwood *Podocarpus latifolius*, which require shady, cool conditions for seedling growth and are very sensitive to fires.

Eventually the forest patch will be large enough to resist most fires, although its advancing front is repeatedly driven back. Under constant pressure of fire, many of the pioneering forests on Table Mountain have never expanded much beyond their original size.

The forest margin is like the wall of a besieged city, and very occasionally its defences do fail. As it sweeps through the forest, fire eliminates the sensitive forest specialists, such as yellowwood and stinkwood, but the sprouters are able to survive by sending out new branches from the base. The prevalence of such multi-stemmed trees and the paucity of forest specialists suggest that many of the Table Mountain forests have been conquered by fire at some stage during their history.

Global weather changes and veld management practices determine whether the forests expand their territory or are driven back into their strongholds by the advance of fynbos plants in the wake of fire. Scientists now believe that many of the characteristic features of fynbos, such as fine branching and the retention of dead material in the canopy, might in fact be adaptations aimed at making fynbos flammable. In the battle against forests, it is certainly a successful strategy.

## FIRE MANAGEMENT

When he rounded the Cape in 1497 Vasco da Gama named South Africa *Terra de Fume* because he saw the smoke of so many fires. Some might have been natural fires, but many would have been lit by the Khoi-khoi inhabitants of the Cape to improve the grazing for their cattle and fat-tailed sheep, and to encourage the spread of watsonias, as they harvested the bulbs as a source of starch.

Much later, colonists from the relatively fire-free deciduous woodlands of western Europe brought their dread of fire to the Cape Peninsula. A 1687 placard warned of the penalties for setting fire to the veld: "For the first offence, severe scourging; a second offence to be punished with the cord until death do follow."

Organised efforts to control fires on the Cape Peninsula started in 1949 with the creation of the Cape Peninsula Fire Protection Committee. Fire lookouts were manned around the clock and fire-fighters were on constant standby, but as the human population increased so did the frequency of fires.

The areas around the city bowl have been especially susceptible to fires, so it is not surprising that at least three proteas have been lost from these areas. The silky-haired pincushion *Leucospermum vestitum* still occurred on the slopes of Lion's Head in 1886, but is now extinct from the Peninsula. Burchell's sugarbush *Protea burchellii*, which once occurred on the shale-derived soils of Signal Hill and Devil's Peak, met with a similar fate, and until the recent "rediscovery" of a dozen plants in the saddle between Table Mountain and Devil's Peak, the red sugarbush *Protea grandiceps* was also listed as extinct from the Peninsula. Proteas were often collected by early botanists, so good records exist of their former distribution, but far more of the less conspicuous plants and animals have no doubt been annihilated by overly frequent fires.

Most fires, therefore, have to be extinguished in order to keep within the natural fire frequency to which plants are adapted. Frequent fires are also

**1** *Clinging precariously to the steep northern precipices of Table Mountain, this is one of the few* Protea grandiceps *plants still surviving on the Cape Peninsula. Formerly common, the species is thought to have been the victim of overly frequent fires.*
**2** *A fire on Signal Hill meets a watery end. Most of the fires on the Cape Peninsula have to be extinguished in order to keep within the natural fire frequency to which fynbos plants are adapted.*

3

blamed for the soil erosion that has left deep scars on the slopes of Devil's Peak and Lion's Head and caused damage to property in places. Erosion is part of a natural process of soil renewal, but the large-scale erosion of denuded slopes after fire can have long-term negative impacts. Early policies of total fire exclusion were specifically aimed at curtailing soil erosion.

At the other extreme, the complete exclusion of fire can result in the extinction of plants that fine-tune their life cycle to the fire cycle. It was only in the late 1960s, however, that botanists began to understand the relationship between fire and fynbos. Until that time, even prominent botanists such as Harry Bolus and Margaret Levyns considered the effects of fire on fynbos to be primarily deleterious, and in his 1951 book on Table Mountain, Carl Luckhoff is vehement in his repeated condemnation of wild fires or prescribed burning of any kind. But with the eventual acceptance of the vital role of fire in fynbos, a programme of prescribed burning was introduced in the 1970s. The Peninsula was divided into blocks that were subject to burning on a 10 to 20 year rotation, although multiple land ownership made co-ordination of activities almost impossible.

The main aim of many prescribed burns is to keep the fuel loads low, and thus prevent uncontrollable fires. Because of the risk to people and property, the burns are kept fairly small, and are often conducted on windless days in spring or early summer, before the vegetation has become dry. In contrast, natural fires would typically occur in autumn on hot, windy days.

All fires, whether deliberate or accidental, have long-term consequences that will be noticeable for many years after the event itself. The details of the fire – the season, age of the veld, the wind speed and direction, the size of the burnt area, and the weather that followed it – will all influence the future vegetation of the area. It is by deciding when and where to light or put out fires that people have their greatest influence on the natural areas of the Cape Peninsula.

3 *Firefighters stand back from the wall of heat emanating from an unusually hot fire in a stand of Australian rooikrans Acacia cyclops. Most of the invasive aliens on the Cape Peninsula come from areas of the world where fire is a regular phenomenon, so these plants come pre-equipped with adaptations such as fireproof cones, ant-dispersed seeds, and fire-stimulated germination, which allow them to flourish in the fynbos environment.*

# Delicate Partnerships

For the past two days it has been stretching and unfurling. Now, at the start of a brilliant summer's day, the first red disa of the season is fully open. At first it remains unnoticed. Then a majestic brown butterfly wings its way up the valley and, after hesitating momentarily, swoops down to settle on the flower. Although the butterfly has never before seen a red disa, some deep instinct has attracted it to the flower and it unrolls its tongue in anticipation.

After sipping nectar from the disa it takes to the air again, but now with yellow pollen packets glued to its legs and thorax. In the weeks that follow, the butterfly will perform the important task of pollination as it carries such pollen packets, called pollinaria, from flower to flower. The pollinated flowers will give rise to fruits containing the seeds of the next generation of red disas. The orchid is completely dependent on these butterflies for its continued existence.

Early naturalists at the Cape were intrigued by the red disa *Disa uniflora*, and endeavoured to find the elusive insect that serves as its pollinator. The mystery was solved in 1895, when Rudolf Marloth captured a specimen of the mountain pride butterfly *Aeropetes tulbaghia* with pollen from the red disa attached to its legs. This was the first evidence of the remarkable partnership between Table Mountain's largest butterfly and its most splendid flower, which quite co-incidentally is also known as the Pride of Table Mountain.

With a wingspan of some 80 millimetres, the mountain pride is so large that in flight it can be mistaken for a small bird. It is easily recognised by its chocolate brown wings decorated with blue "eyespots", which may serve to confuse would-be predators. Apart from its habit of resting on shady stream banks at midday, it is highly active and notoriously difficult to capture. It is found on the mountain only during late summer, which may explain its preference for shady habitats and its need for copious quantities of nectar.

The butterfly is in fact one of the keystone species in the ecology of Table Mountain. If it were to disappear, several plant species that depend exclusively on the mountain pride for pollination would face extinction. Other than *Disa uniflora* these include the cluster disa *Disa ferruginea*, the nerine or Guernsey lily *Nerine sarniensis*, and the red crassula *Crassula coccinea*. All have one feature in common: red flowers.

Colour appears to play a central role in attracting the mountain pride. Indeed, many hikers first encounter this butterfly when it swoops down to inspect clothing in various shades of red. This fixation for the colour red seems to be a unique behavioural feature of the mountain pride. Most other insects cannot even perceive red as a distinct colour – bees, for example, confuse red with grey – and it is for this reason that red flowers are virtually absent from the European flora, which is dominated by insect-pollinated species. Birds, however, have good perception of the colour red, and many of the bird-pollinated plants in the Cape have red flowers. By being able to find these flowers the mountain pride butterfly is able to discover their rich nectar supplies.

The pollination of red flowers by the mountain pride butterfly is just one of the many fascinating partnerships between plants and animals on Table Mountain. In this chapter we take a closer look at these partnerships, and show that the continued survival of many plants is dependent on insects and other pollinators.

***OPPOSITE:*** *A mountain pride butterfly* Aeropetes tulbaghia *inserts its proboscis into the narrow flowers of* Crassula coccinea *to reach their ample supply of nectar.*
**1** *Victorian naturalists searched for 20 years before they discovered the pollinator of the red disa* Disa uniflora *– the mountain pride butterfly.*
**2** *A colourful pageant of red disas alongside a stream on Table Mountain.*
**3** *Caught in the act, a mountain pride butterfly robs nectar from the flowers of* Watsonia tabularis, *designed for bird pollination.*

*1* In an exchange of mutual benefit, a pierid butterfly sips nectar from Micranthus flowers. Pollen on the butterfly is deposited onto the stigmas of the flowers, an essential prelude to seed production.
*2* In the first spring after a fire, a range of bulbs from the iris family, including the pink Ixia scillaris *and the locally rare* Lapeirousia corymbosa, *vie for the attention of pollinators on Signal Hill.*

## FLOWERING SEASONS

Table Mountain does not have a dramatic show of spring flowers as, for example, in Namaqualand and the woodlands of Europe. Certainly, more plants bloom during the spring and summer months, but a wide variety of flowers can be found throughout the year. Even during the cold and rain of winter, when most bees are dormant in their nests, and butterflies and other flying insects are in their larval stages, a surprising number of plants are in flower. Species of *Oxalis*, in particular, brighten up patches of barren ground in the soggy landscape, and many *Protea* species begin flowering in June, their bird pollinators remaining active throughout the winter. From August, "berg winds" bring warmer interludes between the cold fronts, and many insects use these brief windows of opportunity to search for food in flowers.

In September the mountain comes to life with colourful displays of geophytes, such as *Watsonia* and *Gladiolus* species. Bees awaken from their winter slumber and go back to work, collecting pollen and nectar from the flowers of *Polygala bracteolata*, *Wachendorfia paniculata* and numerous other species. Kreupelhout pincushions *Leucospermum conocarpodendron* brighten the mountain slopes, their yellow flowerheads providing nectar for large numbers of sugarbirds and sunbirds.

The floral extravaganza on Table Mountain continues throughout the summer and only begins diminishing towards the end of February. But like a fireworks display the season ends dramatically. Brilliant red flowers of *Disa uniflora* burst out along mossy stream banks and shady clefts, and a suite of blue flowers – *Selago serrata*, *Aristea major* and *Agapanthus africanus* – match the sky in intensity.

By autumn it seems the mountain has exhausted itself. Only the hardiest plants manage to flower, among them species such as *Amaryllis belladonna*, *Nerine sarniensis* and *Cyrtanthus ventricosus*, which have all the water and resources needed for flowering stored underground in large bulbs.

## THE FLORAL MARKETPLACE

In the summer months, colourful flowers stand shoulder to shoulder in the fynbos and the air is filled with heady perfumes. Insects move hurriedly between flowers, searching for hidden nectar and pollen. This is the floral marketplace, where insects shop around for food and, in exchange, provide the service of pollination.

To attract pollinators, flowers need an effective advertising strategy. Brightly coloured petals are like billboards, catching the attention of passing insects. Yellow and blue are particularly effective in attracting bees, so *Nemesia versicolor* has flowers of both colours, while the various *Oxalis* species tend to use either pink or yellow colour schemes. Red flowers entice birds and some butterflies, but white flowers are best for attracting moths as they stand out in the gloom of evening. Monkey beetles prefer yellow and orange flowers, such as those of the sour fig *Carpobrotus edulis* and the little star *Spiloxene capensis*.

Flowers are often decorated with radiating lines or circles of contrasting colour, which guide insects to the nectar hidden within the flower. Particularly beautiful and elaborate nectar guides are found in *Pelargonium*, *Gladiolus* and *Moraea* flowers, but some are as simple as the three orange dots in *Wachendorfia paniculata*, or the "bull's eye" target in *Spiloxene capensis*. *Hebenstretia repens* has only a small orange dot on the flower to guide butterflies to its nectar, while *Aristea spiralis* has a star-shaped nectar guide specially designed for long-tongued flies. Some flowers even have secret nectar guides that reflect mainly ultraviolet light, so they are unseen by humans but clearly visible to some insects, such as bees. Once a flower has been pollinated, it has no further need for pollinators. Flowers of the keurtjies *Podalyria calyptrata* and *Podalyria biflora* develop a white mark on the petals after pollination, which is a signal to bees that their services are no longer needed.

Flowers also attract insects by smell. Honey-scented species such as the blombos *Metalasia muricata* and keurtjie *Podalyria calyptrata* are irresistible to bees, while flies are drawn to the foetid stench of *Orbea variegata* and *Ferraria crispa*. Even after dark, fragrant perfumes attract moths to their favourite flowers.

The floral marketplace is full of thieving insects, which bite through the sides of flowers to steal nectar without performing pollination in return. Many fynbos flowers are protected against these "nectar robbers", some by having thick bracts or sepals to reinforce the base of the flower. The leaves of *Satyrium* orchids encircle the stem and often fill up with water, forming a moat that effectively prevents ants from meddling with the flowers. Perhaps the most innovative means of preventing nectar robbery is the sticky coating on the flowers of many *Erica* species. This not only makes it almost impossible for ants to climb into the flower, but also gums up the mouthparts of bees when they try to bite a hole through its side.

Plants, too, are capable of sometimes committing fraud. These nefarious species advertise boldly, bidding for the services of hungry insects, but their flowers are empty. Pollinators would soon learn to avoid these cheats, but they are fooled completely because the flowers mimic other food-producing flowers. One species, *Disa atricapilla*, even falsely advertises sex by releasing the perfume of female wasps, and by doing so co-opts amorous male wasps into pollinating its flowers!

**3** *A hoverfly* Eristalis *feeds on protein-rich pollen from the flowers of* Spiloxene capensis.
**4** *An unwanted visitor, a monkey beetle drags pollen packets across the stigma of* Disa bivalvata, *an orchid adapted for pollination by male spider-hunting wasps. By doing so it may cause hybridisation of orchid species.*
**5** *The bizarre flowers of the orchid* Disa atricapilla *attract males of the sphecid wasp* Podalonia canescens *by mimicking the sex pheromone of female wasps.*

## BLOOMS FOR BEETLES

Some biologists believe that during the Cretaceous period, 140 million years ago, flowering plants were pollinated by beetles. These beetles were flower-feeders, eating not just pollen but petals as well. While feeding, the beetles would have inadvertently transferred pollen from flower to flower, and in this way helped to launch the evolutionary explosion of the flowering plants.

Today there are beetles on Table Mountain with lifestyles similar to those of their ancestors. Blister beetles, such as the CMR beetles (named after their resemblance to the yellow and black attire of a famous military regiment, the Cape Mounted Rifles), specialise in feeding on flowers, and can wreak havoc in a flowering population. Yet close examination of their bodies often reveals the presence of numerous pollen grains – a tell-tale sign that they can also act as pollinators. Another flower-feeder is the beautiful protea beetle *Trichostetha fascicularis*, which feeds on the soft parts of protea flowerheads, as well as on nectar. It is specially equipped with a long snout to reach down to the base of flowers, and a furry tongue for lapping up nectar.

Many of the beetles now found on Table Mountain are not of the primitive flower-feeding variety, but rather refined creatures which cause minimal damage to the flowers they pollinate. Some of the most important pollinators on the mountain are the monkey beetles, a specialised group of scarabs containing hundreds of species. In summer these comical little beetles can be found buried so deep in flowers that only their long back legs are visible.

**1** *Doing more harm than good, a blister beetle feeds on the petals and anthers of* Gladiolus angustus. *The flower is adapted for pollination by long-tongued flies, but the blister beetle nevertheless transfers some pollen on its wing covers.*

# Empty promises

The bright colours of flowers usually serve to advertise the presence of nutritious pollen or nectar for insect pollinators. But some colourful orchids cheat by not producing nectar. One such fraudulent orchid on Table Mountain is the cluster disa *Disa ferruginea*. It closely resembles the flowers of *Tritoniopsis triticea*, a favourite source of nectar for the mountain pride butterfly *Aeropetes tulbaghia*. The butterfly is evidently fooled by the mimicry, because it repeatedly visits the empty flowers of the disa where it grows alongside the irid *Tritoniopsis*, although it shows little interest in the orchid in areas where it grows alone.

Incredibly, the cluster disa has evolved a different form of mimicry in the Langeberg mountain range in the southern Cape. Here the orchid secures visits by the mountain pride butterfly by imitating the orange nectar-producing flowers of the red-hot poker *Kniphofia uvaria*.

**1** *The mountain pride butterfly* Aeropetes tulbaghia *feeds on nectar from the iris* Tritoniopsis triticea.
**2** *The cluster disa* Disa ferruginea *does not produce nectar, but attracts the mountain pride butterfly by mimicking* Tritoniopsis.

Monkey beetles have an almost magnetic attraction to bright colours, especially yellow, orange and red. For example, yellow daisies such as the gousblom *Arctotis acaulis* and the yellow iris *Ixia dubia* are favourites of these beetles. Yet there are also one or two species that prefer blue flowers like *Roella ciliata.*

Although many monkey beetles are lethargic and appear to like nothing more than lazing about in flowers, there are some species which rush about in the sunshine from flower to flower in a frantic search for food and mating partners. When they do find a mate, they remain *in copula* for more than an hour. It is easy to tell the sexes apart, as in most species it is only the males that have very long back legs, which they use as fighting tools. The amusing appearance of two monkey beetles fighting belies the serious nature of the contest – the victor that succeeds in tossing his rival out of a flower has a better chance of mating with a female.

Sometimes what appears to be a beetle in a daisy will be revealed as a clever imitation on closer inspection. The function of these strange

**2** *A glittering beetle makes a meal of the pollen in an* Ixia *flower.*
**3** *The enlarged hind legs of these male monkey beetles, coated in pollen, are used for earnest shoving battles. Losers are unceremoniously tossed out of the flower. Monkey beetles spend most of their day in yellow and orange flowers, such as these* Ixia dubia *irises.*

**1** *A female monkey beetle embeds herself in a* Gazania pectinata *flower, commonly called the beetle daisy because of its beetle-like markings. Monkey beetles use flowers as a convenient rendezvous for mating.*
**2** Gazania *flowers also attract small* Megapalpus *bee-flies that feed on both pollen and nectar.*
**3** *Attracted by the giant yellow flower of a sour fig* Carpobrotus edulis, *a monkey beetle feeds on pollen in the anthers.*

beetle-like markings has long puzzled biologists. The most remarkable example is in the daisy *Gorteria diffusa*, found only in Namaqualand, which appears to mimic beetles by having dark and shiny bumps of an elaborate structure on its petals.

Several flowers with beetle-like markings are found on Table Mountain, the most striking being *Gazania pectinata*, an orange daisy that flowers in September. The patterns bear an uncanny resemblance to female monkey beetles, so it is not too far-fetched to hypothesise that they serve as decoy females to attract males, which in their haste to mate will pollinate the flower.

But there is another possible explanation. Dark spots on flowers are known to attract small bee-flies *Megapalpus capensis*, and close examination of the flowers of *Gazania pectinata* may often reveal these insects on the "beetle markings". In fact, bee-flies were recently shown to be responsible for pollinating *Gorteria diffusa* in Namaqualand, and on Table Mountain they visit *Pelargonium* species with small black spots on the petals. So perhaps *Gazania*

and other "beetle daisies" should more accurately be called "fly daisies"!

**FOETID FLOWERS**
Some flowers on the mountain would never be included in a bridal bouquet, because even when fresh they are brown and shrivelled, and have a smell to match their deathly appearance. These are the "carrion flowers", pollinated by insects which have larvae that feed on rotting flesh.

On Table Mountain carrion flowers occur among several plant families. The orchid *Satyrium bracteatum*, found on wet rock ledges on the southern slopes of the mountain, produces flowers with a powerful odour of rotting flesh. Carrion flies, such as *Scatophaga stercororia*, eagerly crawl into the flowers, seeking the source of the foetid odour, but stumble into a booby-trap: on bumping into a small projection, small pollen packets become glued to their eyes. There is nowhere suitable to lay eggs, so the hapless flies crawl in vain from flower to flower, pollinating each one in the process.

The iris family's *Ferraria crispa* also has flowers that imitate the appearance and smell of rotting meat. The flower lasts only a day, but carrion flies have no trouble finding it soon after it unfurls in the morning, filling the air with the stench of death. The flies eagerly taste the petals and before long find a small drop of nectar at the base of each. As they position themselves to drink, bright orange pollen is dabbed onto their backs, only to be rubbed off later on the feathery stigma of other *Ferraria* plants. The flowers wilt a few hours after pollination and seeds begin to develop within.

The succulent *Orbea variegata* is perhaps the most convincing in its imitation of rotting flesh. Its flowers, which lie sprawled on the ground, give off a penetrating, nauseating odour, and the petals have a corrugated and mottled surface, resembling the hide of a long-dead animal. Flies find this combination irresistible. As they crawl into the centre of the flower, perhaps searching for a way into the innards of a corpse, pollen packets become affixed to their tongues. An intricate mechanism allows them to be removed by the next flower, completing the process of pollination.

## FUNGUS FLOWERS

A delicate smell reminiscent of mushrooms is emitted by some flowers on Table Mountain, luring fungus gnats of the families Mycetophilidae and Sciaridae, which lay their eggs in mushrooms or rotting vegetable matter. These flowers make their appearance during winter and early spring, at a time when both mushrooms and gnats are fairly abundant.

For example, the orchid *Satyrium bicallosum*, which blooms early in September, has tiny white flowers that attract a minute fungus gnat known as *Sciara*. When the gnat crawls into a flower it touches the sexual organs, and tiny pollen packets become glued to the top of its thorax. Another

orchid, *Liparis capensis*, is so small and inconspicuous that it often escapes the attention of human observers, but its gnat pollinators have no trouble sniffing it out.

The Bibionidae or March flies (a misnomer, as these flies occur in September in the southern hemisphere) are a group of small flies related to fungus gnats. They can be found on a wide variety of flowers, feeding on nectar with their tiny mouthparts. The flowers of the orchid *Disa obtusa* have a pungent odour that attracts *Bibio* flies in large numbers, a boon for predators such as crab spiders and the ant *Camponotus niveosetosus*, which lie in ambush at the flowers.

*4 An iris with a difference, the mottled flowers of* Ferraria crispa *produce a foul stench that attracts flies (5), their chief pollinating agent. The flowers last only a day.*
*6 The orchid* Satyrium bracteatum *has a nauseating smell of rotting flesh and an appearance to match. Attracted by this combination, a carrion fly soon has the orchid's pollen packets stuck firmly to its eyes.*
*7 The flowers of* Orbea variegata *frequently go unnoticed by human passers-by, but not by flies,*

*which locate them by their strong carrion-like odour and appearance.*
*8 Mistaken for a mushroom, the orchid* Satyrium bicallosum *attracts tiny fungus gnats, one of which can be seen disappearing into a flower.*

Although the common mottled horsefly or blind-fly *Haematopota ocellata* has a short tongue and does not as a rule visit flowers, three other horsefly species are important as pollinators on Table Mountain. *Philoliche rostrata*, a large grey fly with a proboscis up to 40 millimetres long, is a pollinator of *Gladiolus carneus*, *Disa harveiana* and *Pelargonium myrrhifolium*, while *Philoliche angulata*, a shiny black fly with a white band on its abdomen, is frequently observed pollinating the common bloodwort *Wachendorfia paniculata*, as well as pelargoniums such as *Pelargonium cucullatum*. A third species, *Philoliche elegans*, pollinates a wide variety of plants.

Both male and female long-tongued horseflies suck nectar from flowers, but the female is also a bloodsucker, her painful bite a familiar annoyance to most mountain walkers. After landing on a suitable mammalian host, she shifts her long nectar-feeding mouthparts to one side, and then inserts a stabbing mandible into the skin at a shallow angle. The lacerated tissue begins to bleed, and she spends a minute or more sucking blood from her hapless victim.

Tanglewing flies are also important pollinators in the Cape fynbos. The most abundant species on Table Mountain is *Prosoeca nitidula*, which we have observed visiting *Gladiolus carneus* and *Pelargonium cucullatum* during November and December. Another species common during October is *Prosoeca westermanni*; although little is known about its flower preferences, we have found it pollinating *Adenandra villosa*, which has short flower tubes matching the fly's stubby proboscis.

The flats around the base of Table Mountain are the natural habitat of the world's most remarkable

In general, a strong odour is characteristic of fly-pollinated plants. The small white flowers of *Rhus* species have a strong semen-like odour, attracting hundreds of tiny flies that serve as pollinators.

### LONG-TONGUED FLIES

A zoological curiosity on Table Mountain is the abundance of long-tongued flies. Remarkably long sucking mouthparts have evolved in two fly families – the horseflies (Tabanidae) and the tanglewing flies (Nemestrinidae) – in southern Africa. These flies, typically the size of large bees, have needle-like mouthparts that can be more than three times the length of their bodies!

Flowers visited by long-tongued flies have nectar hidden at the base of a deep tube, which closely matches the length of its pollinator's tongue. The flowers usually also have nectar guides to help the flies aim their long tongues through the tube's narrow entrance.

**1** *Pollen packets attached to the head of this horsefly* Philoliche rostrata *originate from the flowers of the orchid* Disa harveiana *(2). The disa has no nectar, but relies on its similarity to other long-tubed nectar-producing flowers to trick the flies into visiting it.*

**3** *Seeking to quench its thirst, a horsefly* Philoliche angulata *probes a blood-wort flower* Wachendorfia paniculata *for nectar.*

fly species: *Moegistorhynchus longirostris*, a tangle-wing fly with a nectar-sucking tongue measuring up to 80 millimetres, nearly five times the length of its body! It used to be common, but has apparently been eliminated from most of its former habitat, although it still occurs on the west coast and at Rondevlei. Because flies cannot roll up their tongues like butterflies do, *Moegistorhynchus* tucks its tongue between its legs in flight, trailing it behind its body. On approaching a flower, the tongue is swivelled forward, but manoeuvring this unwieldy appendage is no easy task and the flies often appear clumsy as they attempt to insert it into a flower.

A number of Cape plants are adapted to use this fly as their pollinator, most having flowers with long, slender nectar tubes. The orchid *Disa draconis* does not produce nectar, but it secures visits from the fly by closely resembling other nectar-producing flowers, such as *Pelargonium longicaule*.

It has only recently been established that *Moegistorhynchus longirostris* is the sole pollinator of at least ten plant species on the west coast flats. Some of these species, such as *Ixia paniculata* and *Lapeirousia anceps*, still occur in the Cape Town area at Rondebosch Common and Milnerton Racecourse, but since *Moegistorhynchus* has not been observed there in recent years it may just be a matter of time before these plants follow their pollinator into extinction. Increasing coastal development north of Cape Town also threatens the existence of this fly and its dependent host plants. Unfortunately, it is hard to garner public support for a fly, even one as spectacular as *Moegistorhynchus longirostris*.

### FLOWERS WITH A NIGHTLIFE

After dark, it is the moths that take centre stage, pollinating flowers such as *Struthiola dodecandra*, *Pelargonium triste*, *Crassula fascicularis* and the orchid *Satyrium bicorne*. Most have pale flowers that are easily seen in the dark, and long, narrow tubes in which the nectar is concealed. Some, such as *Zaluzianskya capensis*, remain tightly closed during the day and unfurl just after dusk to reveal their white petals, but most remarkable is *Gladiolus*

*liliaceus*, which somehow changes the colour of its flowers from reddish brown during the day to pale mauve towards evening.

Almost all moth-pollinated flowers emit a sweet and sometimes spicy fragrance in the evening that attracts moths over long distances. The flowers of the orchid *Disa ophrydea* are dark beetroot in colour, so are presumably scarcely visible to moths, yet their powerful scent ensures that their pollinators discover them.

Most of the moths on Table Mountain are not highly selective in the species they visit, and are small enough to settle on flowers while feeding. These moths are the adult stages of caterpillars known as cutworms (family Noctuidae) or loopers (family Geometridae).

The much larger hawkmoths (family Sphingidae) are rarely seen on Table Mountain. These magnificent creatures hover while feeding, and are important pollinators of large white night-scented flowers in much of the rest of Africa. The only plant on Table Mountain that is known to be hawkmoth-pollinated is *Bonatea speciosa*, a large orchid found near the coast at places like Camps Bay and Sandy Bay. When visited by the Cape hawkmoth *Theretra capensis*, a beautiful green moth with red underwings, it glues large pollen packets to the moth's eyes!

It is commonly believed that hawkmoths pollinate the flowers of *Gethyllis afra*, found on Signal Hill and Rondebosch Common, probably because

5

6

8

7

9

**4** *The giant tanglewing fly* Moegistorhynchus longirostris *guides its long tongue into the narrow tube of a pelargonium flower. Pollen packets on the fly's tongue are from the orchid* Disa draconis *growing nearby.*

**5** Geissorhiza tenella *is one of a large group of plants pollinated by* Moegistorhynchus longirostris (**6**).

**7** *All glued up, pollen packets from the orchid* Disa ophrydea *dangle from the tongue of a moth.*

**8** *Flowers of the orchid* Satyrium bicorne *produce a delightful spicy fragrance that fills the evening air and entices moth pollinators.*

**9** *At sunset, the flowers of* Pelargonium lobatum *start to exude a cinnamon odour that attracts moths to their long-tubed flowers.*

Marloth included a painting of a hawkmoth feeding from these flowers in his book *Flora of South Africa*. This must be a mistake, because although the flowers of *Gethyllis* are white, they do not have a narrow tube to accommodate the tongues of moths, nor do they contain nectar.

### BEES – A LIFE AMONG THE FLOWERS

No group of insects is more dependent on flowers for food than the bees. Adults derive all their energy from nectar, while the larvae are fed a mixture of nectar and pollen collected by the females.

The richest diversity of bees is found in the semi-desert regions of the world, and even in the drier inland regions of the Cape there are far more bee species than along the coast. On Table Mountain the diversity of flowering plant species is not reflected in a diverse bee fauna, and it is unlikely that there are more than 300 species. A possible reason for this is that the coarse-grained, sandstone-derived soils are unsuitable for nest-building by many of the solitary species.

Nevertheless, bees pollinate several hundred fynbos species on Table Mountain, particularly those members of the legumes (Fabaceae), sages (Lamiaceae), heaths (Ericaceae) and irises (Iridaceae) that have blue, yellow, pink or white flowers. The nectar is usually fairly accessible in short floral tubes, although sages and legumes have complex flowers which need to be prised open, a task that is not difficult for these intelligent insects.

#### The Cape honeybee

Honeybees are the only truly social bees on Table Mountain. Other bee species, though they may occasionally share nests, live a solitary existence, without any social organisation.

The natural distribution of the Cape honeybee *Apis mellifera capensis* coincides closely with the boundaries of the Cape fynbos, but research by biologists at Rhodes University has established that the centre of distribution, where the purest form of the race occurs, is Table Mountain.

Several unique reproductive and behavioural

*1 The long arms of the orchid* Bonatea speciosa *are designed to glue pollen packets onto the eyes of hovering hawkmoths.*

*2 One of nature's wonders, the flowers of* Gladiolus liliaceus *change from reddish brown during the day to a more visible pale mauve at dusk, when they are visited by moths.*

*3 A honeybee bites through the side of the bird-pollinated flower of* Erica plukenetii *to steal nectar.*

*4 A honeybee sips nectar from the flowers of* Utricularia capensis, *a carnivorous plant that grows in wet seepage habitats on the mountain.*

*5* Erica baccans *is adapted to bee pollination.*

*6 The hinged anthers of* Salvia africana-caerulea, *triggered by the probing action of a bee, bend forward to dab pollen on its back.*

traits have evolved in the Cape honeybee. The most interesting is the ability of unfertilised workers to lay eggs which develop into either workers or queens, rather than drones as in the African honeybee *Apis mellifera scutellata*. The Cape honeybee also forms clusters to generate heat during the cold, wet winters – behaviour that it shares with the European honeybee, but not the African honeybee. By maintaining the hive at a warmer temperature than the surroundings, the bees are able to ensure the rapid development of their young. Honeybees can also reduce the temperature in the nest by fanning the entrance with their wings.

Cape honeybees usually nest in wooded ravines, but occasionally nests are found in rock clefts in open areas. While wild, or feral, colonies of honeybees certainly do exist on Table Mountain, many honeybees originate from hives, probably with negative consequences as they compete with other wild bee species for the limited nectar in flowers.

At certain times of the year, especially during autumn, Cape honeybees may become aggressive and attack for no apparent reason. In general, however, only people with an allergy to bee stings need be concerned when in the vicinity of bee colonies.

### Carder bees

The orchid *Disa tenuifolia* flowers after fire, and in ideal conditions can carpet the ground with its yellow flowers. Patches of the flowers are soon patrolled by small male carder bees *Immanthidium immaculatum*, which chase away all intruders in their territories. Although the flowers lack nectar, this does not deter the bees, which on their patrols go from flower to flower, pollinating them in the process.

7 *Hinged petals protect the pollen and nectar of* Aspalathus *flowers from thieves by allowing access only to powerful carpenter bees, such as this male* Xylocopa caffra, *which is able to prise open the flowers.*

# Buzz pollination

Orphium frutescens is an attractive shrub that grows near the coast on the Cape Peninsula. During summer the plants are covered with robust pink flowers which have a conspicuous cluster of bright yellow anthers at the centre. These attract carpenter bees, which perform a curious ritual on the flowers. They wrap themselves tightly around the cluster of anthers and vibrate their wings for about two seconds, producing a loud buzzing sound, before flying off to repeat the process on the next flower. This is an example of a fascinating process which is known as vibratile or buzz pollination.

Several plant species on Table Mountain are buzz-pollinated, all of them having poricidal anthers – essentially pollen-filled containers with a tiny aperture at the tip – and stigmas which are displaced to one side. Pollen is released through the pores only when the anthers are shaken vigorously. The complex behaviour required to do so increases the likelihood of the pollen being delivered by a specialised pollinator to a flower of the same species.

The large yellow anthers of buzz-pollinated species always look invitingly full of pollen, but carpenter bees avoid flowers which have already been buzzed by other bees. It is not clear how they distinguish between "virgin" and buzzed flowers, although there is evidence that they can detect scents left by other bees. Another possibility is that they simply observe the condition of the flower. In *Orphium*, visited flowers can easily be identified by the dishevelled state of the anthers after vibration.

The flowers of the Christmas berry *Chironia baccifera* are too small for carpenter bees, but are buzz-pollinated by smaller anthophorid bees. The lady's hand *Cyanella hyacinthoides* may also be buzz-pollinated, as it has the characteristic poricidal anthers and displaced stigma, but its pollinator has not yet been caught in the act.

1 *By tightly grasping the anthers and vibrating her wing muscles, a yellow-banded carpenter bee* Xylocopa caffra *releases a cloud of pollen from an* Orphium frutescens *flower during buzz pollination.*
2 *The anthers are twisted closed to keep in the pollen, allowing it to exit only via small pores at the apex.*

**1** *A female oil-collecting bee* Rediviva peringueyi *carries the yellow pollen packets of the oil-producing orchid* Pterygodium catholicum *from flower to flower.*

**2** *The rare orchid* Pterygodium inversum *is one of about 30 plants on the Peninsula that depend on oil-collecting bees for their pollination.*
**3** *A cross-section through a branch reveals the nest compartments of a carpenter bee.*
**4** *Hovering on guard, a male carpenter bee* Xylocopa caffra *stakes out a fiercely defended aerial territory.*
**5** *The empty flowers of* Disperis capensis *(left) are thought to mimic the nectar-producing ones of* Polygala bracteolata *(right) to secure visits by pollinating carpenter bees.*

### Carpenter bees

Contrary to popular belief, there are no bumble-bees (genus *Bombus*) in South Africa. The large bees often mistaken for them are in fact solitary wood-mining or carpenter bees, belonging to the genus *Xylocopa* (family Anthophoridae). They make their nests in the dry wood of dead shrubs, particularly favouring the blackened skeletons of proteas that remain after fire. Although the individuals of some species are known to share nests, carpenter bees are solitary in the sense that they do not depend on each other for survival.

The bees live for up to a year and usually reproduce only once. The female bores a tunnel in the wood, in which she lays as many as 12 large eggs, each accompanied by a small "loaf" of pollen and nectar that is food for the larva after it has hatched.

Carpenter bees are surprisingly common on the Cape Peninsula and are very important pollinators.

Three species are especially significant on Table Mountain – the yellow-banded carpenter bee *Xylocopa caffra*, the lesser black carpenter bee *Xylocopa rufitarsus*, and the giant black carpenter bee *Xylocopa capitata*, the largest of them all.

The yellow-banded carpenter bee *Xylocopa caffra* is ubiquitous on the mountain. The female is easily recognised by her black coat and two conspicuous yellow bands on her abdomen and thorax, while the male is equally distinctive with his completely yellow coat. In spring, mating begins in earnest. The males set up their territories, which they guard by hovering in one place for long periods of time and chasing away any potential rival or intruder.

The list of flowers that depend on carpenter bees for pollination is a long one, and includes various species of *Polygala* and *Aspalathus* as well as several orchids, including *Disa racemosa*, *Disa graminifolia* and *Disperis capensis*. The pink flowers of the keurboom *Virgilia oroboides* are pollinated almost exclusively by *Xylocopa capitata*.

Carpenter bees are also capable of stealing nectar from flowers that are adapted to other pollinators. They often bite holes through the side of long-tubed *Erica* flowers to reach the nectar within. It is possible that the sticky coating on these flowers clogs up the mouthparts of carpenter bees, preventing them from stealing the nectar.

### Oil-collecting bees

The presence of oil in flowers was first discovered in tropical plants in 1969, and has since been recorded in the flowers of South African twinspurs *Diascia*, as well as several groups of orchids.

On Table Mountain, oil is found in the flowers of the orchid genera *Pterygodium* and *Corycium*. Orchids that produce oil tend to have yellow-green flowers with a pungent soapy smell to attract their pollinators – a specialised group of bees in the genus *Rediviva*, which have modified front legs bearing long hairs for mopping up oil. The bees are thought to use the oil as food for their young and for waterproofing their nests, but they also visit other flowers for nectar, such as the yellow flowers of *Moraea ramosissima*.

Most species of *Disperis* produce oil, but there is one species on Table Mountain – *Disperis capensis* – that has empty flowers, secreting neither nectar nor oil. It mimics the appearance of *Polygala bracteolata*, which it grows alongside, so as to fool small carpenter bees (especially *Xylocopa rufitarsus*) into pollinating it. In fact, about one third of all orchid species cheat by not giving food rewards to their pollinators, and instead rely on various ruses to attract pollinators.

6

7

**6** *The nectarless flowers of the blue disa* Disa graminifolia *use their sweet scent to attract ignorant carpenter bees in search of new food sources.*
**7** *A carpenter bee* Xylocopa rufitarsus *bites through the side of a* Pelargonium triste *flower for easy access to its nectar.*

**1** *With a narrow, curved bill and a remarkable hollow tongue, a male orangebreasted sunbird sips nectar from the tubular flowers of* Erica coccinea.

1

## FLOWERS FOR THE BIRDS

Early morning is a magical time on the mountain. A pale orange sky glows behind the distant mountains of the Boland, and the fynbos glistens with dew. The cheerful call of a sunbird breaks the silence as it flits from flower to flower in the half light of dawn.

Sunbirds begin feeding early when flowers are brimming with nectar, as its sugar content is essential in providing the birds with their daily calories. Birds have very high energy requirements compared to insects, so plants must provide copious quantities of nectar if they are to attract birds to their flowers. However, sunbirds do not live entirely on nectar; they also feed on insects that are either plucked from flowers or caught on the wing to fulfil their protein requirements.

Table Mountain has three resident sunbird species. These play a key role in the ecology of the mountain, as they pollinate the flowers of at least 50 different plant species, ranging from bulbs such as *Haemanthus coccineus*, to the bizarre parasitic "cat's nails" *Hyobanche sanguinea*, and the large tree-like kreupelhout pincushion *Leucospermum conocarpodendron*.

Malachite sunbirds *Nectarinia famosa* are the largest sunbirds on the mountain, and also the least common. The males are an iridescent green and have long tail feathers, while the larger females are olive-brown above and pale yellow below. Malachite sunbirds are found mainly on the lower slopes where they visit the flowers of pig's ears *Cotyledon orbiculata*, wild dagga *Leonotis leonurus* and *Salvia africana-lutea*, to name only a few, as their relatively long bill can reach the nectar of most flowers on the mountain.

Orangebreasted sunbirds *Nectarinia violacea* are much smaller, weighing in at about 10 grams – equivalent to two teaspoons of sugar. They are essentially fynbos birds with a distribution restricted to the Cape Floral Kingdom. On Table Mountain they are usually encountered on the upper slopes, where they are important pollinators of long-tubed ericas, such as *Erica coccinea* and *Erica abietina*. Their nests, which are frequently found in kreupelhout bushes *Leucospermum conocarpodendron*, are made with infinite care, usually lined with fluffy parts of protea flowerheads and bound together with spider webs. Sunbirds are monogamous and the males help with feeding the young.

Lesser doublecollared sunbirds *Nectarinia chalybea* are not limited to fynbos habitats but also occur in coastal thickets, where they pollinate flowers such as the candelabra *Brunsvigia orientalis*, as well as in forest patches, where they visit

2

the flowers of the tree fuschia *Halleria lucida*, among others.

Sunbirds are highly effective pollinators. Unlike insects, they are all-weather animals that visit flowers throughout the year, and are able to fly long distances, carrying out cross-pollination between widely distributed plants. Flowers pollinated by sunbirds usually have long tubes, sometimes curved, to conform to the length and shape of the bird's bill, which must be plunged so far down the tube that the head is dusted with pollen.

No sight and sound could be more representative of the fynbos than that of a sugarbird perched on top of a protea bush, cackling raucously to announce its presence, with its long tail streaming in the south-easter. Cape sugarbirds *Promerops cafer* are found only in the Cape Floral Kingdom and have a particularly close relationship with the protea family. On Table Mountain they are often observed on *Protea lepidocarpodendron*, *Protea cynaroides*, *Mimetes fimbriifolius* and *Leucospermum conocarpodendron*, although these are just a few of the many plants they visit. The birds have a long bill and brush-tipped tongue specially adapted for feeding on nectar, which they supplement with insect prey.

Cape sugarbirds are highly territorial animals.

*2 Cape sugarbirds look to proteas for providing nectar, convenient perches, nesting material and nesting sites; in exchange they pollinate the protea blooms.*
*3 Orangebreasted sunbirds seldom venture into strandveld or renosterveld, where ericas are absent. Here a male reaches into an Erica mammosa flower.*

3

# Sunbird services

A few years ago, Steve discovered that some of the orchids found on Table Mountain are pollinated by sunbirds. While birdwatching, he noticed something unusual attached to the bill of a lesser doublecollared sunbird. When he was able to get close enough, he saw that it was a clump of orchid pollinaria. He returned later with Mike Fraser, the well-known ornithologist and author of *A Fynbos Year*, and together they were able to capture some of the sunbirds in mist nets. Steve identified the pollinaria as belonging to *Satyrium carneum*, a large pink orchid that grows in sandy habitats, particularly on the Karbonkelberg and the slopes of Little Lion's Head above Sandy Bay.

All three sunbird species on the Cape Peninsula have now been observed to visit the flowers of *Satyrium carneum*. The nectar is

hidden in two long spurs, and as the sunbirds feed the pollinaria become firmly glued to the upper mandible of the bill. This clearly irritates the birds, as they can often be seen scraping the bill vigorously against branches in an attempt to remove the pollinaria, to no avail.

More recently, Anton discovered that some members of the milkweed family, until now thought to be entirely insect-pollinated, are also pollinated by sunbirds. Milkweeds have parcels of pollen, much like those of orchids, which are attached to the pollinator by a mechanical clip. A microscopic groove on the clip catches on a bristle or some other fine appendage on an insect's body when it visits the flower.

The bokhoring *Microloma sagittatum*, a climber that is fairly common on the Cape Peninsula, has unusual flowers that remain in a bud-like state with the petals twisted together. The only access into the flower is through five tiny, slit-shaped pores, which insects would be unable to find or stretch open. The lesser doublecollared sunbird, however, is adept at locating these slits. It thrusts the tip of its bill through them, and extends its tongue into the bottom of the flower to reach the nectar.

As in all sunbirds, the nectar is drawn up by the tongue, which is frayed at the tip and rolled into twin tubes. Anton examined the tongues of captured sunbirds under a microscope, and found pollen parcels clipped onto the frayed edges. The pollen parcels are evidently carried inside the bird's mouth to the next flower, where they are mechanically detached by the complex structure inside. This is the first record of pollen being transferred on bird tongues.

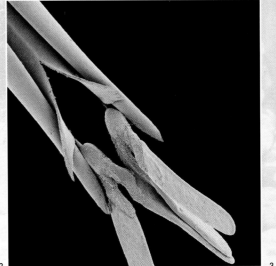

**1** *A male lesser doublecollared sunbird probes the sealed flowers of the bokhoring* Microloma sagittatum. *As it reaches down to sip the nectar, yellow pollen parcels attach themselves to the frayed edges of the tongue (**2**) as shown in this artificially coloured micrograph. The flowers of* Satyrium carneum *(**3**) glued a clump of pollinaria to the bill of this juvenile sunbird (**4**).*

## POLLINATION BY MICE

The publication in 1978 of a report showing that mice are involved in the pollination of proteas caused a sensation in the botanical world. The much-lauded discovery was made by two botanists, John Rourke and Delbert Wiens, who were investigating the pollination mechanisms of the ground-flowering proteas. Acting on a hunch, they trapped mice near a flowering population and found protea pollen in their fur – proof that the mice had visited the flowers.

The male spends much of his time surveying his territory from a high vantage point on a bush, and will chase other birds away. His long tail feathers are believed by some biologists to be a mate-attracting device, while others argue that they serve an important balancing function. Breeding takes place during autumn on Table Mountain and the nests are usually conveniently situated within a flowering protea bush.

Sugarbirds have been shown to be more effective than sunbirds in pollinating the flowers of *Mimetes hirtus*, and the same is probably true of the other *Mimetes* and *Protea* species on the Peninsula. This is because sugarbirds usually cling to a branch and bend over to feed on the flowers, with the result that pollen is smeared over their throat region, whereas sunbirds typically probe sideways into the flowers, without brushing off any pollen.

Sadly, overly frequent fires have reduced the extent of protea veld on Table Mountain, and sugarbirds are probably much less common than they were in the past.

Flower-feeding birds require nectar all year round, so it is fortunate that in the fynbos there are plants in flower in all seasons. During winter, flowering *Protea* shrubs provide the most important source of food for birds, but are replaced in spring by a succession of *Mimetes* and *Leucospermum* bushes, as well as many bulbs, such as the "rotstert" *Babiana ringens*. Late summer and autumn are the driest times of the year, and many sunbirds move higher up the mountain where moisture provided by the "tablecloth" allows a multitude of heaths to continue flowering in profusion. Cape sugarbirds, on the other hand, fly across the Cape Flats in search of flowers when times are hard on the Peninsula, but may return to the same flower patch every year.

Instead of having showy flowers like most bird-pollinated proteas, those of ground-flowering species are dull-coloured and hidden inside bushes. They also produce a strong yeasty odour that acts as a powerful attractant for nocturnal rodents, allowing them to locate the proteas' rich source of nectar in pitch darkness. The mice force their heads deep into the flowerheads and are dusted with pollen, which they will inadvertently transfer from flower to flower.

It is now believed that at least 20 *Protea* species rely on mice for pollination. One of these – *Protea acaulos* – occurs on Table Mountain, and has cryptic, green flowers that smell like rancid stinkbugs! The creeping legume, *Liparia parva*, which is found only on the southern Peninsula, may also be rodent-pollinated, as its flowers are borne close to the ground and produce a musky odour, although its close relative *Liparia splendens* has showy flowers that are pollinated by birds.

**1** *Commonly known as a "rotstert" or rat tail, the odd leafless twig of* Babiana ringens *is in fact a custom-designed perch for the comfort of visiting sunbirds.*
**2** *Thrusting its bill into the flowerhead of the pincushion* Leucospermum conocarpodendron, *a Cape sugarbird performs its vital role of pollination.*
**3** *The concealed flowers of* Androcymbium eucomoides *are believed to be adapted for rodent pollination.*
**4** *Under the cover of darkness, a spiny mouse* Acomys subspinosus *gingerly drinks nectar from a flowerhead of* Protea acaulos.

# Plant-Animal Warfare

When the English explorer William Burchell heaved his way to the summit of Table Mountain in 1810, he came across a silent world of plants swaying in the wind. "I saw no bird of any kind, and but few insects, but the deficiency in zoology was compensated by a rich diversity of botany," he wrote in his journal. This first impression has been shared by thousands of tourists who have expressed disappointment at the absence of large animals on the mountain.

Table Mountain does in fact have a fascinating animal fauna, but it is also true that animals are not as abundant here as they are in a typical African game reserve. The reason for this is simply that fynbos vegetation, which covers most of the mountain, is difficult for animals to eat, the leaves being tough and nutrient-deficient. Those herbivores that do live on Table Mountain are a small band of highly specialised creatures, ranging from leaf-feeding caterpillars through to browsing antelope and subterranean molerats.

When a herbivore bites into a leaf, it deprives the plant of some of its ability to produce food for itself. Each leaf is a tiny green factory, harnessing the energy of the sun to produce starch in a process known as photosynthesis. Plants must therefore protect their leaves against damage by herbivores, their first line of defence being the equivalent of armour-plating or razor-wire fortifications. Many fynbos plants have leaves that are tough and leathery, as in the proteas, or sharp-edged and prickly, like those of the climber's friend *Cliffortia ruscifolia*. The leaves of arum lilies *Zantedeschia aethiopica* are filled with shards of calcium oxalate crystals, causing agony to most animals that try to eat them.

On Table Mountain, some of the plants most sought after by herbivores belong to the pea family Fabaceae. These plants, such as *Aspalathus chenopoda*, have special symbiotic bacteria on their roots that boost the uptake of mineral nutrients, increasing the nutritive value of their leaves. This makes them highly attractive to herbivores, so it is not surprising that they are among the spiniest of plants on the mountain!

Even if their physical defences are breached by herbivores, some plants have a formidable array of chemical weapons in their armoury. The leaves of most fynbos plants are heavily stockpiled with polyphenols, which makes them both unpalatable and indigestible. Some also produce potent poisons, ranging from cyanide in the wild peach tree *Kiggelaria africana*, to heart poisons in the milkweed *Asclepias crispa* and liver poisons in daisies belonging to the genus *Senecio*. Other highly toxic plants that are found on Table Mountain include the chincherinchee *Ornithogalum thyrsoides*, the tulps *Moraea* and *Homeria*, the pig's ear *Cotyledon orbiculata* and the April Fool or blood flower *Haemanthus coccineus*, the bulbs of which were historically used for medicinal purposes by the Cape's indigenous inhabitants. In fact, many modern and

*OPPOSITE*: The ongoing battle between plants and the animals that eat them is no less lethal underground. Many bulbs fall victim to the tusk-like incisors of Cape molerats Georychus capensis, *but some defend themselves with potent toxins.*
**1** *A caterpillar nibbles the soft leaves of* Rhus rosmarinifolia, *a rare find among the generally tough fynbos shrubs.*
**2** *A parrot-beaked tortoise* Homopus areolatus *sizes up the tasty flowers of* Oxalis purpurea.
**3** Aspalathus chenopoda *protects its nutrient-rich leaves with needle-sharp tips.*
**4** *Beautiful but deadly, the chincherinchee* Ornithogalum thyrsoides *contains enough poison to kill a horse.*

traditional medicines are derived from the anti-herbivore chemicals in plants, and this virtually untapped resource is often given as a reason why biodiversity should be conserved.

Herbivores have evolved innovative ways of overcoming the chemical defences of plants, and even some of the most potent toxins can be rendered harmless by specialised herbivores. In response, plants have developed still more potent defences, resulting in a natural "arms race" over the millennia. In this chapter we look at some of the combatants in the biological war between plants and animals on Table Mountain.

## HEAVYWEIGHT HERBIVORES

Few large mammals have ever managed to eke out a living in the fynbos vegetation. Although black rhino, elephant and buffalo were recorded in the vicinity of present-day Cape Town, there is no evidence that they ever occurred on Table Mountain itself. These herbivores lived on the lowland plains around the base of the mountain, where the fertile clay soils supported highly palatable renosterveld plants, particularly grasses.

The lower slopes of Devil's Peak were once covered in renosterveld, but were gradually converted to pine plantations by Cecil Rhodes, and later, during the Second World War, to grassy pastures at the behest of Jan Smuts. Today these pastures support a healthy herd of black wildebeest, and are being used for a selective breeding programme to resurrect the zebra-like quagga. They used to support a small herd of eland, but the last lonely male jumped the fence in 1995 and roamed across the mountain for a few days before it was killed in a bungled recapture operation.

In the past, eland may also have occasionally ventured onto the summit of Table Mountain, but they were unlikely to have lived exclusively on the small-leafed fynbos vegetation. Antelope that have managed to survive in the mountains are mostly

*1 Like a ghost from the past, a young eland bull Taurotragus oryx wanders along the slopes of the Apostles after escaping from his enclosure on Devil's Peak. Eland and other big herbivores would once have been common in areas with rich, shale-derived soil, such as the city bowl, where grassy renosterveld flourished.*
*2 Although they never occurred on the Cape Peninsula in historical times, bontebok Damaliscus dorcas dorcas, southern Africa's rarest antelope, have been introduced to Cape Point in an effort to ensure the species' survival. Its original home range in the renosterveld on the south coast plain has been all but destroyed by wheat-farming.*

selective browsers, with narrow muzzles and small bite-sizes to ensure that they don't get a mouthful of twigs with the leaves they eat. For example, grysbok *Raphicerus melanotis* are still fairly common in bushy areas on Table Mountain. Although they are nocturnal, they are sometimes seen in the early morning or late afternoon. Steenbok *Raphicerus campestris* and duikers *Sylvicapra grimmia* are much rarer on the Peninsula and probably do not occur on the mountain itself, the former having a preference for sandy areas and the latter dense vegetation such as strandveld.

Unfortunately, the most abundant large herbivore on Table Mountain today is the alien Himalayan tahr *Hemitragus jemlahicus*. The population originated from a single pair that escaped from Rhodes Zoo in the 1930s, and grew to about 1 000 animals in 1970, in places causing severe soil erosion from overgrazing. A programme of eradication has reduced their numbers to about 80 animals today, but the elimination of the remaining tahrs has proved difficult because of their superb agility and rock-climbing skills. It is curious that these exotic animals have been so successful on Table Mountain, while local antelope, having had millions of years to adapt, seem barely able to find enough to eat.

1

## PLANT-EATING PRIMATES

Apart from man, the chacma baboons *Papio ursinus* of the Cape Peninsula have the distinction of being the southernmost primates in the world. Here in the nutrient-poor fynbos they have to spend considerably more time foraging than their relatives in the savannahs do. They are expert botanists, capable of distinguishing the poisonous from the delectable and of locating nutritious bulbs by the presence of a single, thin leaf. Flowers, such as those of pincushions *Leucospermum*, the geophyte *Aristea* and the wild sage *Salvia africana*, form part of their diet, as do the large seeds of the rooikrans *Acacia cyclops* and the restios *Hypodiscus aristatus* and *Willdenowia glomerata*. In the strandveld they relish the berries of the skilpadbos *Nylandtia spinosa*, the sea guarri *Euclea racemosa* and the wild olive *Olea europea africana*.

Baboons supplement their vegetable diet with insects, and the males sometimes prey on larger animals. However, the Cape Peninsula baboons are most famous for their unique habit of foraging in the intertidal area. At low tide they prise limpets off the rocks with their teeth, and catch crabs and other shellfish by turning over rocks. The more timid youngsters remain on the beach and catch sandhoppers in the piles of decaying kelp left behind by the retreating tide.

Being opportunistic feeders, baboons will exploit the advantages associated with human settlement. Rubbish bins and picnic sites are an invitation too tempting to resist, and the resulting conflict with

**1** *Life is tough for baboons* Papio ursinus *living in the fynbos. In an environment where there is almost no fruit and few insects, baboons have to spend a large portion of the day foraging. Young baboons (2) learn how to locate edible bulbs and other rare delicacies by imitation.*

2

humans has led to the demise of baboons in the northern parts of the Cape Peninsula, including Table Mountain.

The 350 baboons currently living on the Peninsula are divided into about ten troops, seven of which are confined to the sparsely inhabited Cape Point area. The Tokai troop has the northern-most distribution on the Peninsula, and may ulti-mately recolonise Table Mountain.

## THE GNAWERS

Rodents are the largest and, by some measures, the most successful group of mammals. They occur in almost every part of the world, and have adapted to a vast range of habitats. In this respect, the rodents on the Cape Peninsula are no exception.

The striped mouse *Rhabdomys pumilio* is the most common rodent in the Peninsula's natural areas. It is active during the day, especially in the mornings and late afternoons when it forages for seeds, which are relatively rich in nutrients.

At night, a number of other rodents fill the seed-eating niche. The diminutive pigmy mouse *Mus minutoides*, Verreaux's mouse *Praomys verreauxii* and Cape spiny mouse *Acomys subspinosus* are all common on the Peninsula, while the Cape gerbil *Tatera afra* is restricted to the lower-lying areas of the adjacent flats, where it digs extensive burrow systems in the loose sand.

The dense vegetation of seeps is the chosen habitat of the vlei rat *Otomys irroratus*, a stoutly built rodent with large rounded ears, a blunt face, short tail and shaggy grey-brown coat. Although these rats are diurnal, they are rarely seen, as they live in thick restio beds and when disturbed prove to be both fast runners and strong swimmers, even underwater.

On the Peninsula, their diet consists primarily of restio stalks, which they clip off close to the ground. While feeding, they sit on their haunches and gnaw at a restio stalk held between their front feet, dis-carding the less nutritious bits in small piles. Restios have a very low nutritional value, but are available throughout the year, so vlei rats have small litters of two to three and no pronounced breeding season. The young are reared in a nest made on raised ground from restio stalks and other plant fibres.

The Peninsula's most interesting rodents are subterranean. These are the molerats, a group con-fined to sub-Saharan Africa. They have minute eyes, no external ears, velvety fur, and a short tail fringed with long bristles. Their lips close behind their prominent incisors, so they can use their teeth for digging without getting sand in their mouths. After the soil is loosened with the teeth it is moved back-ward with the feet and pushed out of the burrow, forming characteristic mounds.

This group of mammals is best known for the social systems of some species, but neither of the species that occur on the Peninsula is social. The Cape molerat *Georychus capensis* is common throughout the Peninsula, and even occurs at high

3

4

altitudes on the Back Table. Its habitat preference overlaps to some extent with that of the dune mole-rat *Bathyergus suillus*, which is confined to low-lying sandy areas, such as Rondebosch Common and Rondevlei. Dune molerats are the largest of all subterranean rodents, the males weighing up to 1.5 kilograms. Giant molehills, half a metre high, are evidence of their subterranean activity.

Both species are bulb-eaters, but the diet of the dune molerat also includes the above-ground parts of plants, which are pulled down into the burrow from below and consumed underground. Molerats seem to have a special capacity for tolerating some toxins and will happily feast on the bulbs of several poisonous species, including the chincherinchee *Ornithogalum thyrsoides*, which packs enough

**3** *Usually the only evidence of the Cape gerbil* Tatera afra *is a series of burrow entrances in sandy soil. Unlike typical gerbils, which hop on their hind feet, the large gerbils of the genus* Tatera *walk on all fours.*

**4** *The diurnal striped mouse* Rhabdomys pumilio *is by far the most common rodent in the natural vegetation on the Cape Peninsula. It is typically seen in pairs, darting from bush to bush across open areas.*

1

*1 Back off! The fearsome incisors of the Cape molerat Georychus capensis are its main digging implements, but also serve to protect it against small carnivores and molesnakes. Molerats seldom come above ground, except when dispersing to new areas or when flushed out of their burrows by winter floods.*
*2 Clusters of small bulbs nestle in a cage of thorny roots surrounding the main bulb of Moraea ramosissima. In its attempt to get at the main bulb (3), the molerat dislodges the smaller bulbs, inadvertently facilitating their underground dispersal.*

poison into a handful of its bulbs to kill a horse. However, other toxins, such as those in the large bulb of the candelabra plant *Brunsvigia orientalis*, are clearly effective against molerats.

Nevertheless, molerats probably benefit many bulbous plant species by dispersing their bulbs underground. Cape molerats, in particular, do not consume all the bulbs they find *in situ*, but carry many of them off to underground stores in dead-ends of the burrow system containing as many as 5 000 bulbs. If the food stores are neglected, the bulbs sprout and grow to the surface. This explains

2

3

why some bulbous species occasionally come up in dense clumps.

Several bulb plants on the Cape Peninsula seem to be specially adapted to molerat dispersal. Instead of having a single large bulb, the bulbs of some species consist of segments, rather like cloves of garlic. Molerats break off the segments to feed on them individually, and the undamaged segments are carried back to the store or are lost in the sand. One example is *Micranthus junceus*, which has particularly palatable bulbs that are stored in large numbers by molerats. Some biologists believe that such palatability has evolved in bulbs as a mechanism to attract their subterranean dispersal agents.

*Moraea ramosissima* and *Moraea viscaria*, which are both common on the Peninsula, have taken these adaptations a step further. In the former the main bulb is protected by a cage of thorny roots, outside of which are masses of minute bulbils, each attached to the plant via a thin placenta. In attempting to get at the main bulb, molerats dislodge the bulbils, which are then dispersed throughout the burrow system. The bulbils are essentially genetic lifeboats, ensuring the plant's survival and enabling it to colonise new sites.

Both molerat species on the Cape Peninsula breed in winter and early spring. Males initiate courtship by rapid drumming with their hind feet; the vibrations are detected underground by the females, which drum at a lower frequency in response. The Cape molerat produces about six young in a litter, the dune molerat half as many, and in both species the young disperse at an age of two months.

Porcupines *Hystrix africae-australis* are close relatives of molerats. Along the footpaths on Table Mountain, evidence of their nocturnal activity is often seen, such as a freshly dug hole where a bulb has been unearthed. Scattered in the sand alongside the bulb's discarded husks are the odd quill, lumpy fibrous dropping or distinctive flat-footed print.

Porcupines eat a wide variety of foodstuffs, including fruit and bark, but on the Cape Peninsula they subsist almost entirely on the underground storage organs of plants. The bulbs of members of the iris family, such as *Watsonia* and *Babiana*, *Chasmanthe* and *Romulea*, are a staple food source, and are sniffed out with the keen sense of smell. The tubers of the arum lily *Zantedeschia aethiopica* are another favourite, although how the porcupines tolerate their needle-like calcium oxalate crystals is a mystery. The tubers are also very hard and fibrous, but porcupines make short work of them with their chisel-like teeth.

Porcupines forage only at night, usually alone but sometimes in pairs or small family groups. They are monogamous and produce one to three offspring per year. Family members share a daytime shelter, usually either a cave among the boulders of a scree slope or an extensive burrow dug into firm soil. These dwellings are often scattered with old bones, which are collected by the porcupines and gnawed to supplement the mineral-deficient diet of bulbs.

## A DASSIE'S LIFE

Dassies *Procavia capensis* are peculiar woolly herbivores living on the scree slopes and rocky mountain summits of the Peninsula. In areas of intense human activity, such as the upper cable car station and Cape Point, they are habituated to people and can be observed at close range.

Although they superficially resemble rabbits, dassies are in fact more closely related to elephants. At one time, huge dassies were among the dominant herbivores of Africa, but with the evolution of the competitively superior ungulate grazers they became confined to marginal rocky habitats. Dassies thrive in this difficult terrain, where nutrient-poor, unpalatable plants are the only available food.

Dassies live in harems of as many as 20 females presided over by a single adult male, the younger males being forced to leave when they reach maturity. Such gregarious living has advantages in terms of energy conservation, as the dassies can huddle together to stay warm at night and in cold weather. They also conserve energy by allowing the

4

body temperature to drop several degrees during the night. As soon as they emerge from their crag in the morning, they find a protected place in which to sunbathe, effectively restoring their body heat before they get on with the day's activities.

Dassies feed for only short periods during the day, and then retire to digest their meal, the plant matter being slowly fermented in a large bacteria-filled sac. Indeed, the animals spend most of their time in relative inactivity – theirs is a minimalistic lifestyle aimed at conserving energy in a harsh environment.

On Table Mountain dassies mate in February, and give birth to between one and six young after a gestation period of seven months. Newborn dassies climb onto the backs of adults, with the result that they take on their scent and are recognised as members of the colony.

5

6

*4 After a night of bulb-digging, a porcupine* Hystrix africae-australis *heads for its burrow. The tubers of arum lilies* Zantedeschia aethiopica (**5**) *are a particularly favoured food item.*

*6 The dassie* Procavia capensis *is one of the few herbivores tough enough to survive on a diet of fynbos plants. While other members of the colony feed, a sentry scans for approaching danger (**7**).*

7

**1** *The female* Acraea horta *uses chemical clues to track down the wild peach* Kiggelaria africana, *on which she lays her eggs.*
**2** *Emerging from the relative safety of their silvery eggs, these tiny acraea caterpillars face a battle for survival. The empty egg cases will become their first meal.*
**3** *Spines on the body of this acraea caterpillar contain a cyanide-based toxin that is partly derived from the leaves of its main food plant, the wild peach.*
**4** *An acraea butterfly dries its wings after emerging from its pupal case.*

## LIFE CYCLES OF BUTTERFLIES

While butterflies perform the vital service of pollination for many plants, their larvae – caterpillars – are voracious plant-eaters. Plants and caterpillars are old adversaries, providing some of the best examples of the biological "arms race".

The Cape Peninsula has about 75 species of butterfly, 53 of which occur on Table Mountain itself. Considering that the tough leaves of fynbos shrubs are inedible for most caterpillars, this is a remarkable number – higher than that for the whole of the British Isles. In fact, the butterfly fauna of the entire Cape fynbos region is very different from that of the rest of southern Africa. While the butterflies known as blues (family Lycaenidae) and browns (subfamily Satyriinae) are common, there is only one species of swallowtail (family Papilionidae) and acraea (family Acraeidae), and the large genus *Charaxes* is absent

altogether. Those butterfly groups that have flourished in the Cape tend not to depend on typical hard-leafed fynbos shrubs as a larval food supply, but instead exploit some other more nutritious source of food.

### Acraeas and wild peach trees

The small garden acraea *Acraea horta* is the most common butterfly on the lower slopes of the mountain. It is a slow-moving insect, which can indulge in its lazy ways because it is protected by a bitter-tasting cyanide concoction. Brick-red wings serve as a warning to birds and other predators to avoid this easy target.

The butterflies mate at the height of summer, when clouds of garden acraeas often spill over from the mountain into the surrounding suburbs. The females are generally lighter in colour than the males, and acquire a horn-like protuberance at the tip of the abdomen after mating that blocks the advances of other males. They then seek out the

wild peach tree *Kiggelaria africana* and lay their eggs on its leaves. Although this is a forest tree, abundant on the lower eastern slopes of Table Mountain, it is also common in gardens. The eggs are laid in neat groups of up to 150, and it is not long before the miniature caterpillars hatch and proceed to eat their own shells, following which they start on the leaves. At first they succeed only in scraping at the surface, but as they grow larger they eventually become adept at nibbling the edges.

From birth the caterpillars are protected by rows of spines filled with the noxious cyanide-containing liquid. Biologists believe that the cyanide in acraeid caterpillars, and later in the butterflies, is derived from the leaves of the wild peach, which release the poison's sharp odour when crushed. The anti-herbivore defence system of this tree thus seems to have backfired: by providing the butterflies and their larvae with a means of defence against predators, the wild peach has unwittingly contributed to the success of its chief enemy.

Once they are fully grown the caterpillars abseil from the tree on long silken threads and then crawl towards another tree or rock, where they suspend themselves from a silken pad and pupate. It is in these metamorphic stages that the acraea is most vulnerable to parasitism. In some years, the caterpillars and pupae are so badly infested with parasites that very few survive to become adults, while in other years the parasites are relatively scarce and the butterflies abundant.

### Swallowtails and blister bushes

The handsome citrus swallowtail or Christmas butterfly *Papilio demodocus* is another common butterfly found in midsummer. Easily recognised by its distinctive yellow and black markings, it is a powerful flier that seems to beat its wings constantly, even when feeding on nectar. This is the only member of the swallowtail group of butterflies to inhabit Table Mountain permanently, although there is another species, *Papilio nireus lyaeus*, which has occasionally strayed here from the forests of Knysna and further afield.

In most parts of southern Africa, caterpillars of the citrus swallowtail feed on plants belonging to the citrus family. In the fynbos, however, the citrus family is represented only by species with small, hard leaves, such as the buchus. Since these are virtually inedible to caterpillars, the butterflies on Table Mountain opt to lay their eggs on the larger, softer leaves of the blister bush *Peucedanum galbanum*, a member of the carrot family. The caterpillars seem immune to the noxious substance in the leaves, which in humans causes a painful blistering reaction on the skin following exposure to sunlight. It emanates from oil glands dotted over the surface of the leaf, similar to those on citrus leaves, which may be the common feature that makes the blister bush attractive to the butterfly.

A good place to observe swallowtail butterflies is along the path up to Lion's Head, where the rituals of mating and egg-laying are played out among the abundant blister bushes in midsummer. The female butterfly is careful not to lay all her eggs in one batch, as the voracious young caterpillars would soon compete with one another for the limited food supply. Instead she lays a single egg per leaf, and appears to choose only the healthiest and most tender examples.

The young caterpillars hatch after about six days and, after eating their own egg shells, get straight down to the task of eating leaves. As they mature, the caterpillars undergo a number of changes in appearance. They begin life camouflaged as bird droppings, but since this becomes less convincing as they grow, they assume a mottled green colour that blends in with their leafy surroundings.

They also have some innovative means of frightening off potential predators, which will be explained in the next chapter.

When they reach a length of about 45 millimetres the caterpillars find a sheltered spot among the branches to pupate. Inside the pupae the body contents can be seen reorganising themselves, until the skin splits to reveal the chrysalis which has formed inside. Within the chrysalis further changes take place, until, miraculously, a perfect adult butterfly emerges. The whole process takes about two weeks, except during the winter when the chrysalis remains dormant for several months.

### African monarchs and milkweeds

Striking red and black wings, splashed with white, convey the message to birds and other predators that the African monarch butterfly *Danaus chrysippus*, like the garden acraea, is to be left well alone. Monarch butterflies lay their eggs on the leaves of milkweeds (family Asclepiadaceae), so-named

*Papilio demodocus* caterpillars (**5**) *feed almost exclusively on leaves of the blister bush* Peucedanum galbanum *on Table Mountain. The caterpillars are transformed into the beautiful citrus swallowtail, also known as the Christmas butterfly (**6**).*

**8** *Soon after emerging from its pupal case, an African monarch pumps up its wings, brightly coloured to warn predators that the butterfly is highly poisonous.*

**7** *Making a meal out of a plant that is poisonous to most other insects, a caterpillar of the African monarch butterfly* Danaus chrysippus *feeds on the flowers and leaves of the succulent* Orbea variegata.

# Bodyguards for leaves

Rather than relying solely on the unpalatable nature of their leaves to defend themselves from herbivores, some of the plants on Table Mountain employ their own personal bodyguards to protect these vital organs.

All members of the protea family have tiny red glands at the tips of the leaves, ranging from just a single small gland in *Protea* species, to a row of glands on the leaf margins of *Mimetes* and *Leucospermum*. The glands secrete a sugary liquid similar to the nectar produced by flowers, so biologists refer to them as "extra-floral nectaries".

The nectaries are highly attractive to ants, particularly sugar ants *Camponotus niveosetosus* and pugnacious ants *Anoplolepis custodiens*, which can be seen scurrying from leaf to leaf, pausing momentarily to lick up the glistening fluid. In the same way as flowers produce nectar to reward their pollinators, it is thought that the nectaries provide the ants with sustenance in exchange for their services as bodyguards, driving herbivorous insects away from the leaves.

Several forest trees on the Cape Peninsula use the same principle to attract their own microscopic Mafia family of mites for protection. In this case the reward is a refuge in which to rest, breed and moult, safe inside small pockets on the leaves called domatia ("little houses").

The domatia of stinkwood *Ocotea bullata* are conspicuous blisters on the upper surface of the leaf, which open through hair-fringed slits onto the lower surface. Those of most other plants, including the wild peach *Kiggelaria africana* and the pock ironwood *Chionanthus foveolatus*, are hairy tufts inside shallow hollows on the underside of the leaf.

A microscopic examination of the domatia of stinkwood and pock ironwood revealed that they house minute predatory and fungus-eating mites, but no plant-eating mites. Predatory mites benefit plants by devouring their plant-eating relatives as well as the eggs of insects, while fungus-eating mites graze on fungal threads that cover the leaf surface. By providing them with a shelter, the trees ensure that their bodyguards will be loyal servants in the fight against herbivores.

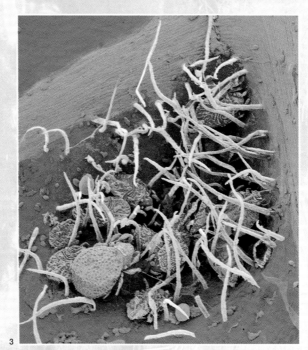

**1** *Perched on the leaf hairs of the pincushion Leucospermum conocarpodendron, an ant Camponotus vestitus licks a sugary secretion from shiny red glands. The presence of ants on the leaves may protect the plant from harmful insects such as caterpillars.*

**2** *Tiny pockets on the leaves of many species, such as this stinkwood Ocotea bullata, were recently shown to house predatory and fungus-eating mites that act as bodyguards for the plant.*

**3** *Inside the hair-lined pockets of the pock ironwood Chionanthus foveolatus, a fungus-eating mite rests amid the discarded exoskeletons and egg cases of former tenants. This picture is an artificially coloured micrograph produced with a scanning electron microscope. It is an 82 X magnification.*

because of the poisonous white latex that oozes from broken leaves. The poisonous component is usually a cardiac glycoside that affects the heart muscles of predators, but North American scientists have shown that it also occurs in the bodies of monarch butterflies, presumably as a result of the caterpillars feeding on milkweed leaves.

The African monarch is the only one of seven southern African monarch species to occur on Table Mountain. Here its caterpillars feed not only on a few *Asclepias* species, but also on the bizarre carrion flower *Orbea variegata*, which is a member of the same family. The milkweed family is not prominent in the Cape flora, and this may explain why the African monarch is not abundant on the mountain.

### Browns and grasses

The Satyriinae, or browns, are drab, inconspicuous butterflies which often go unnoticed, even in habitats where they are relatively abundant. They are mainly grass-feeders, and have been fairly successful in colonising the Cape fynbos. Although grasses are not a major element of fynbos, they are a good larval food source as their leaves are not as hard and unpalatable as those of shrubby plants.

The bland diet of grass means that neither the caterpillars nor the adults are poisonous, so they cannot afford to be highly visible. Instead, the caterpillars rely on camouflage to escape detection by their enemies, typically being dull-coloured and striped to blend into the grassy background. Most hide in the bases of grass tussocks until nightfall, when they emerge to feed. Apart from the reduced threat of predation, it is also possible that the grass blades are more succulent, and the caterpillars at less risk of desiccation, during the evening.

By far the most common butterfly of this group in the Cape is the autumn brown *Dira clytus*, which appears everywhere on the mountain during late summer and autumn, sometimes in congregations of several thousand individuals. The butterflies have eyespots on the wings, which are thought to confer some protection against predatory birds. As is typical of browns, the females scatter their eggs as they fly, so after hatching the caterpillars feed on a wide range of grass species. Adult autumn browns are seldom seen visiting flowers for nectar, but can be spotted by their low and clumsy flight pattern.

In contrast, the mountain pride *Aeropetes*

*1 The autumn brown* Dira clytus, *with its row of protective "eyespots" on the wings, is one of the most distinctive butterflies of the mountain. Females are often seen flying low over grass tussocks, in which they scatter their eggs.*
*2 Known as a skipper because of its erratic flight,* Metisella metis *warms up in the morning sun. It belongs to the Hesperiidae, a "primitive" family of butterflies with many moth-like characteristics. At night the skipper caterpillars feed on grasses, and during the day hide inside a tube constructed by binding the edges of a grass blade together with silk.*

*tulbaghia* is a powerful flier and often visits red flowers for nectar. Adults are on the wing between December and April, which coincides with the appearance of many of the red flowers on Table Mountain. The females are easily distinguished from the males by the three, rather than two, yellow bands on the forewing. Although the caterpillars have been successfully reared on several grass species, including *Ehrharta erecta* and *Hyparrhenia hirta*, it is not yet known which grasses on Table Mountain are the caterpillars' most important food plants. The pupae have been found attached to ferns and other plants growing beneath overhanging rocks.

**1** *The diminutive "blues" and "coppers", such as this* Aloeides pierus, *belong to the family Lycaenidae, and are the most common butterflies on the Peninsula. The caterpillars of most species are associated with ants during the larval stages, and some are even carried into the ant nest.*
**2** *Emperor moth caterpillars* Imbrasia cytherea *feed on a wide variety of indigenous plants, but they have also become a pest in pine plantations, hence their common name – pine emperors.*
**3** *A caterpillar of the moth* Brithys crini *eats its way through a seed capsule of the March lily* Amaryllis belladonna. *The caterpillars are apparently immune to the toxic alkaloids found in members of the amaryllis family.*

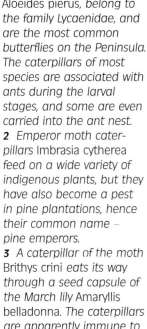

### Lycaenid butterflies and ant nests

More than half of all the butterfly species on Table Mountain belong to the Lycaenid family, which includes the blues and coppers. One, with the delightful name of "skiereilandskollie" or Peninsula ragamuffin *Thestor obscurus*, has the distinction of being the only butterfly species that is endemic to the Cape Peninsula.

Most blues and coppers are small and have shimmering wings. Nearly all of them are associated during their larval stages with ants, which relish the sugary secretion produced by special glands on the caterpillars. In some species the caterpillars feed mainly on leaves and are tended by ants above ground, but in others they are carried back into the ant nest, where they become carnivorous and consume the ant brood!

*Capys alphaeus* is one of the few lycaenid butterflies that has no known association with ants. It is dependent instead on proteas, hence its common name, the protea scarlet. The caterpillars feed on the relatively nutritious and succulent flowerheads of the proteas, and then pupate in them, so they are deplored by commercial protea farmers. The protea scarlet is said to have become less common on Table Mountain; this is attributed to overly frequent wildfires that have reduced the numbers of protea plants.

### Cutworms, emperors and hawks

Moths, like most butterflies, are dependent on plants to provide food for their larvae, but are less specific in their choice of host plant. In fact, the larvae of moth species occurring on Table Mountain have found a way to eat some of the least edible plants in the world.

Bulbous plants of the amaryllis family are among the most toxic on the mountain, yet they are fed on by some small caterpillars that are completely immune to their poisons. These are the larvae of *Brithys crini*, a widely distributed moth that occurs as far north as southern Europe. Although the adults are unremarkable creatures with dark brown forewings and light hindwings, the caterpillars are colourfully banded with yellow and black. They bore out the inside of flower stalks, causing them to collapse, and even feed on soft, fleshy seeds.

**4** The beautiful coat of the Cape lappet moth caterpillar Pachypasa capensis, feeding here on a Cliffortia species near the coast, is not just for decoration. The multi-hued hairs provide warning coloration that is enhanced by the caterpillars' behaviour of clustering together during the day (**5**); after dark they disperse to feed.

5

4

*1  A thyretid moth,* Thyretes
hippotes, *lays her eggs on
the broad, sword-shaped
leaf of* Watsonia borbonica,
*which will soon be notched
by nibbling caterpillars.*
*2  Under cover of darkness,
a hawkmoth caterpillar*
Hippotion eson *feeds on an
arum lily leaf. Its snake-like
appearance and large "eyespots" are enough to scare
off all but the boldest of
predators.*

Despite being associated with introduced pine trees, on which its caterpillars are a pest, the pine emperor moth *Imbrasia cytherea* is indigenous to South Africa. On Table Mountain its main host plant is the taaibos *Rhus angustifolia*, but the caterpillars have quite catholic tastes and have been recorded on *Watsonia*, *Myrica* and even *Protea* species. Close up, the caterpillars can be seen to be covered with a mosaic of tiny coloured scales. When fully grown,

at a length of nearly 10 centimetres, they leave the host plant and search for suitable soft ground to burrow into and pupate, remaining in this state for up to six months. Like all members of the emperor moth family Saturnidae, the adults do not feed after they emerge, and only live for a few days. Relatively few species of emperor moths occur in the Cape region, and only the pine emperor is common on Table Mountain. The best-known South African species is probably the mopane moth *Gonimbrasia belina*, as its caterpillars are relished as a delicacy in the Northern Province.

The caterpillars of the Cape lappet moth *Pachypasa capensis*, belonging to the family Lasiocampidae, must be among the best-dressed insects on the mountain, as they are adorned with a multi-hued coat of hairs. Their relatives the tent caterpillars, the larvae of the moth *Bombycomorpha pallida*, are dark, hairy caterpillars that live in large colonies in communal nests spun from silk. They feed on the lower slopes of Table Mountain, but are also a pest on exotic pepper trees in suburban gardens.

The arum lily *Zantedeschia aethiopica* is a food plant of several hawkmoth species on Table Mountain. The caterpillars, which are hairless and have a spine at their rear end, have voracious appetites, and can each consume an entire arum leaf in one night! *Hippotion eson* has such a close relationship with the plants that it is known as the arum lily hawkmoth.

## SAPSUCKERS

Sapsuckers have one of the most innovative modes of feeding among insects. Instead of contending with the virtually indigestible leaves of fynbos plants, these vampires of the insect world suck body fluids from their host. Long, tubular mouthparts allow them to drill into the plant tissues in search of a "vein" filled with energy-rich sap. Most sapsuckers are bugs belonging to the order Hemiptera, which includes such familiar insects as aphids, stinkbugs and cicadas, all of which feed on plant sap or (more rarely) animal blood.

The renosterbos *Elytropappus rhinocerotis* is often found with small patches of a foamy substance, colloquially known as "cuckoo spit", on its stems. Underneath the foam is a small, stout insect with its sharp mouthparts firmly inserted into the stem. This is the spittle bug, one of the most common sapsuckers on the mountain.

Plant sap generally contains more sugar than sapsuckers need, but large quantities of sap must be imbibed to meet their protein requirements. As a result, sapsuckers excrete copious quantities of a sugary waste product. In aphids this waste substance is the "honeydew" so eagerly sought after by ants, but spittle bugs use it instead to construct their foamy nests. The abdomen of the spittle bug acts like a pump, contracting back and forth to secrete the waste liquid, at the same time forcing air into it to give the foamy consistency.

The foam prevents the spittle bug from desiccating in the hot Cape summers, and also gives some protection against predators. When fully grown, the spittle bug develops wings and is known as a froghopper, as it can jump powerfully if disturbed.

Few insects make their presence known as emphatically as the cicada. The male's shrill mating call is one of the most characteristic sounds on a hot day in the African bush. Notoriously difficult to locate, its apparent ability to throw its voice like a ventriloquist is achieved by constantly changing the call's frequency. Cicadas are found mostly in densely wooded parts of Table Mountain, but they are not as common here as elsewhere in southern Africa. They are classic sapsuckers, tapping into the veins of trees with mouthparts tough enough to penetrate thick layers of bark.

## THE MOUNTAIN COCKROACH

Cockroaches instil feelings of revulsion in most people, who associate them with dirty and unhygienic conditions. Yet the Cape mountain cockroach *Aptera fusca* is a delightful, clean-living insect which lives in fynbos vegetation on the mountain. It is thought to have a very general diet of leaves, decomposing plant material and possibly even the remains of dead insects. The entomologist S.H. Skaife, who had a house on the slopes above Hout

3

4

**3** *Female Cape mountain cockroaches* Aptera fusca, *which are much larger than the winged males, can often be seen sunning themselves in the afternoon. If threatened, the female makes a squeaking sound and sprays a chemical that stains human skin red.*
**4** *Singing as it sucks, a cicada* Platypleura capensis *emits its high-pitched mating call while drawing sap from the stem of a renosterbos* Elytropappus rhinocerotis. *Females of the species must have more luck in locating these accomplished ventriloquists than human searchers.*

Bay, even observed a mountain cockroach eating the fruits of the parasitic dodder *Cuscuta nitida*.

Mountain cockroaches are commonly encountered on Table Mountain, climbing on plant stems or scurrying through the undergrowth. In both sexes the body is flattened so they can creep beneath bark or under stones, but the males are slender and winged, while the females are large, wingless and covered in articulated plates, rather like an armadillo. The females are known as "squeakers", because when disturbed they make a high-pitched sound by rubbing the articulated plates together. Occasionally they are seen with a brood of youngsters. Unlike most insects, the young cockroaches are born live, and remain with their mother for the first few weeks of their life. Such parental care is highly unusual among insects.

## GRASSHOPPERS, LOCUSTS AND CRICKETS

Swarms of locusts regularly decimate huge swathes of vegetation in Africa, leaving famine in their wake, but the fynbos vegetation on Table Mountain is unpalatable enough to keep them at bay. Only after a fire, when the new vegetation is relatively succulent and edible, are locusts and grasshoppers relatively abundant.

Bladder grasshoppers are among the most spectacular and interesting of all grasshoppers. The male has a greatly inflated and transparent abdomen, with a rough protuberance that he rubs his hind legs against to produce a loud, shrill call. *Bullacris discolour* can often be heard calling for mates on warm summer nights on both Signal Hill and Constantiaberg. Some of the smaller males prefer to remain silent – their strategy is apparently to intercept the females before they reach their calling competitors. Although the females are not inflated, they do produce a soft response call, almost inaudible to the human ear.

Crickets, which are even more renowned for their nocturnal serenading, share the order Orthoptera with the locusts and grasshoppers.

*OPPOSITE: An armoured cricket or "koringkriek" Hetrodes pupus feeds on the flowers of Protea lepidocarpodendron.*
*1 Even with their powerful jaws, grasshoppers struggle to subsist on the tough, leathery leaves of fynbos plants.*

# Sydney Harold Skaife (1889-1976)

S H. Skaife, South Africa's most famous entomologist, had a long association with Table Mountain. He arrived in Cape Town from England in 1913, and immediately became enchanted with the Cape Peninsula, describing it as a naturalist's paradise. Skaife worked in Natal for a number of years, but eventually settled in Hout Bay, where he built a house in the shadow of Table Mountain. Many of his observations of Peninsula insects were made in the extensive grounds of this property and its immediate vicinity.

Skaife was one of those rare scientists with a gift for communication, both written and spoken, and he did more than any other person to convey the charms of South African insects to the general public. In a delightful series of essays in the *Cape Times*, published as *South African Nature Notes* in 1932, Skaife gave insights into the behaviour of many animals on Table Mountain. Other books followed, including his magnum opus *African Insect Life* published in 1953, *Dwellers in Darkness*, on the life of termites, in 1955, and *The Study of Ants* in 1961. However, to many generations of South Africans he is best remembered for his wonderful nature-based children's books, such as the *Strange Adventures* series.

In the early days of radio broadcasting Skaife gave talks on various natural history subjects, and he later became Director of School Broadcasting, a post he held until he retired in

UCT ARCHIVES

1945. Skaife was also responsible for the introduction of biology as a subject in secondary schools in the early 1920s. This was not an easy task and he met with stiff opposition, especially from people who feared that he would introduce "Darwinism" into schools.

Perhaps Skaife's greatest achievement was to persuade the authorities to establish the Cape of Good Hope Nature Reserve. Today the Skaife Environmental Education Centre in the reserve is visited by thousands of schoolchildren and students each year. It is a fitting memorial to Skaife's rich and varied life, recounted in his autobiography, *A Naturalist Remembers* (1963).

*Black mound termites Amitermes hastatus, a favourite study subject of Skaife's, construct small tar-black domes throughout the fynbos landscape on the Cape Peninsula. The workers never see sunlight, as they spend their lives tunnelling through the soil in search of humus and dead wood.*

# Hunting and Hiding

Sunlight streaming through the leaves illuminates a chameleon poised, perfectly still, at the end of a branch. A small fly has settled within striking distance and, oblivious to the danger nearby, it begins to preen its wings. Suddenly the chameleon unleashes its tongue, blots up the unsuspecting victim and flicks it back into its mouth. A life has been obliterated in less than one twentieth of a second.

The Cape dwarf chameleon *Bradypodion pumilum* is a lizard that is superbly adapted for a life in trees and shrubs. It moves ponderously through the foliage, the epitome of caution, pausing in places favourable for an ambush. Each foot is equipped with two sets of grasping toes that pinch tightly over small branches, while additional support is provided by the prehensile tail. The eyes, mounted in turrets of skin, are able to focus in two different directions at once, but both swivel forward to give binocular vision when the chameleon is approaching prey. The tongue is at least as long as the animal's body, but is concertinaed onto a special bone at the back of the jaw until it is catapulted forward by muscular action.

Chameleons can change colour, although this ability is often exaggerated. The Cape dwarf chameleon is only able to change from a light apple-green to a dark olive-green. Dark colours absorb more heat, so the chameleon often flattens its body and assumes the dark colour to sunbathe in the early morning. The lighter colour blends in with the foliage, allowing the chameleon to camouflage itself while it lies in ambush or stalks its prey and, perhaps more importantly, to escape detection from predators. As it is such a slow-moving creature, the chameleon is vulnerable to predation, so its last resort if attacked is to hiss menacingly and open its mouth to reveal a bright orange interior.

Most of the predators on Table Mountain today are small and inconspicuous, like the chameleon. Large carnivores were historically never abundant on Table Mountain, and the few that used to occur here disappeared soon after the arrival of the European settlers at the Cape. Perceived as a threat, or simply hunted for sport, lion, leopard and brown hyaena were all eliminated by the early nineteenth century. Yet the diminutive predators which lurk in

the fynbos today engage in hunting behaviour no less spectacular than the "kills" that attract visitors to the game parks of Africa.

**LYING IN WAIT**

Many predators employ the tactic of ambush to capture their prey. Instead of wasting energy in the chase, these hunters play a waiting game, attacking only when their prey is too close to escape. The success of the ambush depends largely on the predator's ability to conceal itself.

Mantids hunt in a similar manner to chameleons, relying on stealth and camouflage to ambush their prey. Their front legs, armed with a row of razor-sharp spikes, are unfolded at lightning speed when a suitably sized insect comes within striking distance.

---

*OPPOSITE: By flattening and darkening its body, a Cape dwarf chameleon* Bradypodion pumilum *makes the most of the winter sun as it chomps on its latest victim, a hoverfly attracted by the flowers of the bietou* Chrysanthemoides monilifera.

*1 The caracal* Felis caracal *is the largest indigenous predator on the Cape Peninsula. It hunts at night, mainly for small mammals such as mice and dassies.*

*2 Demonstrating its ability to swivel its eyes independently, a Cape dwarf chameleon keeps an eye out for predators as it laps dewdrops from a*

*leaf. Dwarf chameleons need to drink frequently, and are sometimes attracted to shiny objects that resemble drops of water.*

*3 Propelled with an almost unfailing accuracy, a chameleon's tongue is used to blot up small insects that wander within striking distance.*

*4 Even the cover of darkness may not be enough to protect insects from their enemies. A small moth unfortunate enough to have fallen prey to the mantid* Sphodromantis gastrica *is systematically dismembered and eaten.*

**1** *Gruesome games of hide-and-seek play themselves out in a Lilliputian world among the shrubs. A mantid stalking a leaf hopper on an everlasting* Syncarpha vestita *might itself fall victim to a keen-eyed grassbird.*

1

1

2

*Named for their ability to scuttle sideways and backwards with ease, crab spiders of the family Thomisidae come in various shades that match the bright colours of flowers. There they lie in ambush for insect pollinators, such as these unlucky flies visiting the sour fig* Carpobrotus edulis *(1) and* Disa racemosa *(2).*

*3 From beast to beauty, a spotted-wing antlion* Palpares speciosus *starts its life as a grotesque grub, then metamorphoses into an elegant, winged adult.*

The prey is skewered and clamped so that it cannot escape, and then eaten alive.

Mantids are known in South Africa by the colloquial names hottentotsgod or praying mantis, because their upright body and folded front legs call to mind a person in prayer. Unlike most insects, their head can swivel, so they can follow the movement of prey with a cold, unblinking stare from their bulging compound eyes while keeping the rest of the body motionless.

Mantids often lurk among flowers, ready to ambush visiting insects. In fact, some South African mantids have become so specialised at this tactic that they have evolved bright pink colours, rendering them almost invisible on similarly coloured blooms. However, those found on Table Mountain, such as *Sphodromantis gastrica*, are generally green

3

or brown and do most of their hunting camouflaged among the foliage.

Crab spiders have perfected the art of ambush in flowers, where they lie in wait for insect pollinators. The abundance of flowers in the fynbos means that there are always plenty of suitable habitats for these cryptic spiders. They are usually white, yellow or pink, but contrary to popular belief they cannot take on the colour of their surroundings, although some species can slowly change from white to yellow over a day or two. Interestingly, their excellent camouflage has been shown to be more important for escaping detection by predators, such as birds, than for ambushing prey.

While insects that land on flowers are liable to fall prey to crab spiders, those that crawl on the ground face a different peril. The pitfall traps of antlion larvae are so effective and deadly that few insects which fall into them survive. Conical in shape and with sides of loose sand, they are almost impossible for small insects to crawl out of. Those unfortunate enough to stumble into the pit slide to the bottom, where the antlion larva lies in wait, armed with a pair of menacing jaws for sucking the juices from its victims. The larva eventually pupates underground, and is transformed into a delicate and attractive flying adult that resembles a large dragonfly, but is distinguishable by the erratic and slow manner in which it flaps its oversized wings.

Rocky outcrops on Table Mountain are nearly always home to two different insect-eating lizards: the southern rock agama *Agama atra* and the girdled lizard *Cordylus niger*. The male rock agama is a flamboyant creature during the mating season, when his head develops a bright blue colour and he shows off by perching on top of a rock and doing press-ups with his front legs. His colourful head bobbing up and down in this teasing manner has earned him the Afrikaans name "koggelmander". He does not tolerate rivals and jealously guards a

**4** *A rock agama* Agama atra *perches on a king protea* Protea cynaroides *in the hope of capturing nectar- and pollen-feeding insects that visit the flower.*

**5** *King of his castle, a male rock agama guards his territory from the top of its highest rock and gets set for some push-ups to show off his bright blue chest to females in the area.*

4

patch of territory, in which the duller female may be seen skulking around. Agamas feed mainly on ants and termites, but catch any insect unfortunate enough to settle within striking range. They are not endowed with a long tongue like chameleons, but are extremely fast over a 50-centimetre dash.

The girdled lizard *Cordylus niger* has a distinctly dinosaurean appearance. The rows of spiny scales along its tail have earned it the affectionate name "Cape crocodile", but unlike its larger reptilian cousins it does not venture near water and spends most of its time sunning itself on rocky outcrops. It is not as bold as the agama, and dives into a rock crevice at the slightest disturbance, where it inflates itself so that the scales lodge it firmly in position. Its diet consists mainly of small insects. The much larger crag lizard *Pseudocordylus microlepidotus* preys on smaller reptiles, including the agamas and girdled lizards, as well as insects such as beetles and grasshoppers. It is probably the shiest of all the Table Mountain lizards, and is almost impossible to extricate from the rock cracks in which it hides.

Snakes are possibly the most misunderstood of all animals, and strike fear into the hearts of many people, whether or not they are venomous species. But in most encounters on the Cape Peninsula, the snake is seen only when it is heading for cover, terrified out of its wits at the booming vibration of heavy mountain boots stomping along the path towards it.

Slug-eaters *Duberria lutrix* are among the commonest snakes on the wet eastern slopes of Table

5

**1** *The small berg adder* Bitis atropos *is seldom encountered on Table Mountain, but its fondness for basking on rock ledges poses some threat to climbers. Its toxin is unusual among adders in having neurological effects rather than a tissue-destroying action.*

Mountain. They live exclusively on a diet of snails and slugs, which they track down by following their slime trails. Egg-eaters *Dasypeltis scabra* have equally specialised diets, and are adapted to feed solely on birds' eggs. They are toothless snakes, but the eggs are broken with enlarged vertebral spines that penetrate into the gullet. Although they are completely harmless, egg-eaters protect themselves by mimicking the markings of the venomous many-horned adder *Bitis cornuta cornuta*, and by striking at attackers and rubbing their scales together to produce an adder-like hiss.

Cross-marked grass snakes *Psammophis crucifer* and Karoo sand snakes *Psammophis notostictus* are slender, fast snakes that are active during the day. They occur in dry, sandy fynbos and strandveld, where they hunt primarily lizards. Spotted skaap-stekers *Psammophylax rhombeatus* also feed on lizards and other small vertebrates. Despite their common name, which translates from Afrikaans as "sheep stabber", they are incapable of killing larger animals. Although the venom is very potent, it is produced in extremely small quantities, and humans generally suffer no ill effects from the bite. The female skaapsteker guards her clutch of eggs until they hatch; such maternal care is unusual behaviour among snakes.

The only snakes that pose significant danger to human visitors to Table Mountain are puff adders *Bitis arietans*, Cape cobras *Naja nivea*, boomslang *Dispholidus typus* and berg adders *Bitis atropos*. Of these, puff adders pose the greatest threat because they are reluctant to move away when hikers approach. Fortunately they are rare on the mountain, occurring mainly on the dry, lower slopes of the Apostles and Karbonkelberg, although they are fairly common at Cape Point. Puff adders are sluggish snakes that ambush rodent prey and inject a powerful cytotoxic venom, which acts by destroying body tissues.

The venom of the berg adder is neurotoxic, affecting the nervous system, and although it is not fatal to humans the bite has relatively serious effects. A rock climber who was recently bitten on Table Mountain suffered long-term impairment of his senses of taste and smell.

Boomslang are fairly common on the mountain. They mainly occur in the forest canopy, but are also often encountered on rocky scree slopes and in open fynbos and strandveld. Boomslang hunt birds, chameleons and frogs, and although their venom is potentially lethal to humans, they are timid snakes that seldom bite.

Molesnakes are often mistaken for poisonous snakes, but they have no venom and are harmless.

2 *A master of deception, a toothless common egg-eater* Dasypeltis scabra *flattens its head into an adder-like shape and rasps the coils of its body together to produce a convincingly threatening hiss.*
3 *A spotted skaapsteker* Psammophylax rhombeatus *guards her clutch of eggs.*
4 *A molerat's worst enemy, the non-venomous mole-snake* Pseudapsis cana *kills its subterranean prey by constriction.*
5 *Beautiful but deadly, the Cape cobra* Naja nivea *is becoming increasingly rare on the Cape Peninsula.*

They do battle with huge molerats in their subterranean burrows and kill them by strangulation, if they are not repelled or even injured by the mole-rats' tusk-like incisors.

## HUNTING AT SPEED

The ability to outrun, outfly or outswim prey is an indispensable asset to a predator. This is true whether one is considering a cheetah chasing a gazelle on the plains of Africa, or a robberfly pursuing a butterfly on the slopes of Table Mountain.

### Warm-blooded hunters

Lions and leopards roamed the slopes of Table Mountain in historical times, but today the caracal *Felis caracal*, weighing in at about 14 kilograms, is the largest predator on the mountain. Also known as the rooikat, it is a handsome animal with black

*1 A large-spotted genet* Genetta tigrina *is caught in the act as it slinks around at night in search of prey. Genets are particularly common in the southern Peninsula, where they occasionally enter houses backing onto the mountain.*
*2 A glimpse is all one usually gets of the small grey mongoose* Herpestes pulverulenta, *a shy but ubiquitous diurnal predator on the Peninsula.*

# Porcupine defences

Few animals are as well defended from predators as the porcupine *Hystrix africae-australis*. Most of its body is covered with needle-sharp quills up to 30 centimetres long, and between these are thinner, more flexible spines that are even longer.

The quills lie flat when a porcupine is at ease, but they can be rapidly erected for a frightening defensive display. With a sudden flash of quills, the porcupine seems to double in size, becoming a bristling ball of spines. At the same time, it grumbles menacingly and stamps its hind feet. The hollow, open-ended quills on long stalks on the tail are loudly rattled and the white rump is exposed, drawing attention away from the head and breast, which are covered only in coarse black hair. A long crest of white-tipped, erectile hairs on the neck enhances the illusion of great size.

It is not all for show either. If threatened, the beast will charge backwards at its assailant, or over longer distances will gallop forwards before turning at the last moment to drive home the quills. The oldest record of this defensive behaviour is a 1660 description by Jean-Baptiste Tavernier of a lion found dead on the slopes of Table Mountain with four porcupine quills in its chest. The skin of the lion, with quills still attached, hung in the Fort for many years.

*1 Quills are a porcupine's impenetrable defence, but they cannot, as the common myth claims, be shot at an assailant.*
*2 Hollow, open-ended quills on long stalks on the tail are used to produce a menacing rattle.*

It may have been finds such as this that led to the popular misconception that porcupines are able to shoot their quills over some distance at assailants – this was disproved as early as 1668 by the naturalist Johan Schreyer, who kept porcupines in his room in order to study them!

tufts on its ears. Although it is shy and nocturnal, most people who spend a lot of time on the mountain eventually get to see one. It occasionally takes birds and lizards but primarily hunts mammals, probably depending largely on dassies and mice on Table Mountain.

The large-spotted genet *Genetta tigrina* also occurs on the Peninsula. At night it hunts mice, frogs, insects and other small animals, and during the day rests in holes in trees and similar shelters, even borrowing a squirrel's drey on occasion. Despite its cat-like appearance, it belongs to a much older group related to the mongooses.

The small grey mongoose *Herpestes pulverulenta* is the most commonly encountered predatory mammal on the Peninsula. It is a low-slung and elongated grey animal with a thick tapering tail that trails behind it when it runs. Because it is active during the day and frequents picnic sites in search of scraps, it often comes into contact with people, but remains skittish. At night, it sleeps in boulder piles and other ready-made shelters. Its diet mainly consists of rodents and insects, which it hunts in a home range of about 60 hectares, but it also eats the eggs of tortoises and ground-nesting birds, cracking them open against a rock with a well-aimed backward throw. Birds are clearly aware of the danger that these small predators pose and are sometimes seen dive-bombing those that get too close to their nests.

### Hunters on the wing

Of course, many birds are also skilled hunters, whether they are large birds of prey or small insectivores. Black eagles *Aquila verreauxii* are the highlight of a walk on the summit of Table Mountain. On routes such as India Venster and Ascension Ravine they often make close passes as they swoop around a corner in the hope of surprising a dassie. Dassies are constantly on the lookout for the birds, and one bark from the sentry, usually an old female, sends the whole colony scurrying into its rock fortress. A special shield in the eye allows dassies to stare straight into the sun, probably a defensive adaptation as this is the direction from which black eagles tend to attack, almost always in pairs and often hunting co-operatively.

Black eagles share the lofty heights and mountain cliffs with rock kestrels *Falco tinnunculus*, which hunt smaller prey, especially rock agamas and girdled lizards. The mountains of the Cape Peninsula also support the highest recorded density of peregrine falcons *Falco peregrinus minor* in southern Africa, with no less than 12 pairs. Each has a home range of between 100 and 200 square kilometres,

3

which overlaps with neighbouring ones by about 20 per cent. Peregrines typically catch their prey by dive-bombing them; with wings folded back, they can reach speeds of up to 380 kilometres per hour before striking their target – usually a bird in flight.

Whitenecked ravens *Corvus albicollis* are fairly common at high altitude, where their rough, grating "kraaaaak" is often heard. They are usually seen hopping around on exposed rocks in an apparently aimless way, or spiralling lazily overhead with the occasional flap of their powerful black wings. Whitenecked ravens eat a variety of animals, both dead and alive, tearing at the flesh with their massive bills.

Steppe buzzards *Buteo buteo* are very common visitors to the Cape Peninsula during summer, migrating from their breeding areas on the Eurasian steppe. They are usually seen sitting on a high perch such as a telephone pole, alert for locusts, small mammals and frogs passing below, but because their plumage is highly variable, they are often confused with other species.

Jackal buzzards *Buteo rufofuscus* are much less common. These chestnut-breasted raptors are occasionally seen soaring over

**3** *The fastest birds on the Peninsula, peregrine falcons* Falco peregrinus minor *drop onto their aerial prey in a blur of speed. Much of their time, however, is spent in inactivity, perched with their mate on a favourite cliff.*
**4** *The black eagle* Aquila verreauxii *is a specialist hunter, with dassies comprising 70 to 90 per cent of its diet on the Peninsula.*

4

*1 All eyes and ears, the spotted eagle owl Bubo africanus scans the darkness for prey, which at Kirstenbosch includes many golden moles and molerats, and even the occasional fruit bat.*
*2 Among the jumble of boulders on the Back Table, a hungry spotted eagle owl chick hisses incessantly to ensure that it will be found by its parents on their return from the hunt. An examination of their pellets – oblong balls of undigested animal parts that the owls regurgitate – suggested that the owls in this area had been feeding largely on frogs.*

areas of broken terrain, where they hunt rodents, francolins and snakes.

Kites prefer low-lying areas such as Rondebosch Common and Smitswinkelvlakte. Blackshouldered kites *Elanus caeruleus* typically hover for lengthy periods before dropping onto a striped mouse or other rodent, whereas yellowbilled kites *Milvus migrans parasitus* are less fussy in their choice of food, eating almost any animal, dead or alive. Both species are very agile in flight.

Redbreasted sparrowhawks *Accipiter rufiventris* and African goshawks *Accipiter tachiro* are primarily forest hunters. Both prey on forest birds by swooping down from concealed positions among the foliage.

At night, the owls take over as lords of the air. Spotted eagle owls *Bubo africanus* are very common throughout the Peninsula and even in the suburbs, where they frequently breed in old oak trees. On the mountain, they breed on rock bands and small cliffs, preying on frogs and small mammals such as bats and rodents. The much smaller wood owls *Strix woodfordii* are fairly common in Table Mountain's forests, where they feed mainly on insects and breed in holes in tree trunks.

On a smaller scale, insectivorous birds hunt with no less skill than the larger birds of prey. Grassbirds *Sphenoeacus afer* dive into dense bushes and restio clumps where they skulk among the green stalks, becoming so preoccupied with feeding that they can be approached at close range. They are the most common insectivorous birds in the fynbos on Table Mountain, and are particularly conspicuous at dusk and dawn, when they call melodiously from atop bushes. Other fynbos insectivores that co-occur with grassbirds are the diminutive neddicky *Cisticola fulvicapilla*, the spotted prinia *Prinia maculosa* and the Cape robin *Cossypha caffra*.

Ground woodpeckers *Geocolaptes olivaceus* are most unusual insectivores. They are true woodpeckers, but have adapted to a treeless landscape by becoming terrestrial. Instead of hammering away at trees in search of grubs, they bounce around on the dry, boulder-strewn slopes of Table Mountain hunting for their favourite prey – ants. They have also forsaken trees as breeding sites and instead dig their nest chambers in the soil. Occurring only at fairly high elevations, they are common on the upper sections of Kasteelspoort and Corridor Ravine, where they are usually encountered as small family parties that attract attention with their harsh screams. Sometimes ground woodpeckers are mistaken for the Cape rock thrush *Monticola rupestris*, which also has a habit of perching on top of boulders and has similar orange tones on the chest, although it is not very common on the Peninsula.

In summer large flocks of black swifts *Apus barbatus* are often seen spiralling high overheard, and on the higher peaks of the Table Mountain range one occasionally finds oneself in the midst of a wheeling cloud of the twittering birds as they feed on small flying insects. Sometimes they are joined by an alpine swift *Apus melba*, unmistakable with its white belly and throat, which is such a fast flier that its wings make a loud whooshing sound as they slice though the air.

Swifts are so honed to their airborne lifestyle that their feet have become too reduced for perching and their wings too long and thin for them to be able to take off from the ground. Even nesting material, which consists of feathers and other aerial flotsam and jetsam, is collected on the wing by the female and then glued onto an overhanging

**3** *Few insects escape the keen eyes of the grassbird* Sphenoeacus afer, *the most common insectivore in the fynbos on the Peninsula.*
**4** *Despite its excellent camouflage, an unlucky cricket becomes a meal for a neddicky* Cisticola fulvicapilla. *Insectivorous birds and cryptic insects are caught in a never-ending evolutionary race in which refinement of the prey's disguise is matched by improvements in the hunter's detection skills.*
**5** *Ground woodpeckers* Geocolaptes olivaceus *are adapted to a treeless landscape, pecking for their living in the soil and even nesting in underground chambers.*

rock face with her saliva. Every summer hundreds of black swifts nest in large colonies in horizontal cracks under the overhanging cliffs of Table Mountain.

Nightjars are the swifts of the night sky. They too hawk insects on the wing, their accuracy improved by an exceptionally wide gape and a fringe of stiff bristles that funnel insects into the mouth. Nightjars are difficult to identify by sight alone, but the fierynecked nightjar *Caprimulgus pectoralis*, which occurs in old fynbos on Table Mountain, is easily recognised on summer evenings by its distinctive "good-lord-deliver-us" call.

On evening walks the spotted dikkop *Burhinus capensis* is also likely to be encountered. It is a large plover-like bird with huge, yellow eyes that provide excellent night vision, allowing it to hunt terrestrial insects in the dark. During the day it crouches in the dappled shade of bushes, well camouflaged by its mottled plumage.

**1** *Cock of its rock, the Cape rock thrush* Monticola rupestris *is a conspicuous species because of its habit of perching on high rocks, but it is not very common on the Peninsula.*
**2** *With feathers puffed up, a female Cape batis* Batis capensis *prepares for a cold night. Batises are forest insectivores that have long hairs around the bill to guide prey into the mouth.*
**3** *The large eyes of the dikkop* Burhinus capensis *are the key to its success as a nocturnal insectivore.*

The bird fauna of Table Mountain's forests has few species in common with the surrounding fynbos. Here the most conspicuous and beautiful insectivores are the flycatchers, particularly the male paradise flycatcher *Terpsiphone viridis*, which has an extraordinarily long, orange-red tail and a bright blue wattle around the eye. The paradise flycatchers arrive on the Cape Peninsula in about September, having spent the winter in the warmer climes of Natal and Mozambique. Soon after arrival they construct their nests in the fork of a forest tree. The cup is built from strips of bark and grass bound with spider webs and camouflaged with lichens. Both parents tend to the chicks, feeding them insects such as dragonflies and cicadas that have been caught in flight. It is quite a sight to see the male trying to follow the erratic flight path of a cicada, with his long tail trailing behind him.

Another member of the flycatcher family, the Cape batis *Batis capensis*, builds a similar though more sturdy nest than that of the paradise flycatcher, and may return to the same clump of trees year after year to do so. The male at first brings the brooding female large food items but, once the chicks have hatched, switches to much smaller insects and spiders, which the female softens in her bill before feeding to the young.

Batises and dusky flycatchers *Muscicapa adusta* have much the same habitat requirements and diets, although they differ somewhat in their hunting methods. While batises are constantly weaving through the leafy canopy or understorey in search of insects, dusky flycatchers prefer to hunt from a low perch, swooping down to pluck up insects with an audible snap of the bill.

### Miniature hunters

Some insects also hunt their prey on the wing, while others give chase on the ground. Robberflies

5

4

6

are well equipped for aerial combat, having powerful wings and large eyes that are surrounded by coarse hairs, probably to protect them from being damaged by thrashing prey. They often hunt from a favourite perch and chase passing insects with a noisy, darting flight. Once they have their victims firmly grasped between their strong legs, they impale them with a short stabbing proboscis and then alight to finish their meal, sucking out the juices before discarding the remainder of the corpse. Bees and monkey beetles seem to be the favourite prey of the species that frequent Table Mountain, but some, such as the forest species *Synolcus dubius*, do not balk at cannibalism.

Adult tiger beetles *Cicindela* are among the most fleet-footed predators on Table Mountain. Like many active hunters they have superb eyesight and are armed with a formidable pair of jaws, which they use like secateurs to catch and then prune insect prey into bite-sized portions. Smaller insects, such as ants, are snatched up and swallowed whole. On hot days, tiger beetles are easy to find along the paths on Table Mountain, and copulating pairs are often encountered. During mating the male grasps the female in his jaws and inserts his long, orange genitalia into her cloaca. This does not seem to disturb the female and she continues her hunting excursions with the male riding on her back!

The larvae of tiger beetles are also predators, but

7

**4** *Mating in Cicindela* tiger beetles *is carried out with the same speed and vigour that is characteristic of their hunting. The male grasps the female in his jaws and it is all over within minutes.*
**5** *Robberflies sometimes capture and kill members of their own species. Here* Synolcus dubius, *a common species on the Peninsula, engages in brutal cannibalism.*
**6** *While an orange-legged robberfly* Laphria flavipes *sucks the body fluids from its victim, bristles around its mouth protect its eyes from injury by flailing legs.*
**7** *Perched on a red disa, a robberfly surveys its streamside habitat for passing prey.*

unlike the free-roaming adults, they wait in ambush at the entrance to their burrows and seize passing insects with their oversized jaws. The burrows, which are vertical tunnels with neat holes opening to the surface, are usually found in the vicinity of the adults, but the larvae are almost impossible to catch sight of as they retreat deep underground at the slightest disturbance.

Competing with adult tiger beetles in the category of fastest hunter on Table Mountain are the strange creatures variously known as solifugids, jerrymunglums, Roman spiders or sun spiders. Solifugids are not insects but arachnids, closely related to spiders and scorpions. They move over the ground at lightning speed, and grasp and subdue their insect prey with a pair of powerful mouthparts. Their long pedipalps are sometimes mistaken for an extra pair of legs, but like other arachnids they have only four true pairs of legs. One species, *Solpuga grindleyi*, is endemic to Table Mountain.

Four species of scorpion are found on Table Mountain, and although some are capable of delivering an extremely painful sting, they are not considered dangerous to humans. The large Cape burrowing scorpion *Opistophthalmus capensis* is restricted to dry areas, and is common on Signal Hill and the lower slopes of the Apostles. It has the characteristic large pincers and relatively slender tail of the family Scorpionidae. Members of this family are not very venomous, and instead use their powerful pincers to subdue their prey. Cape burrowing scorpions construct their burrows in loose sand, with the entrance hidden under a rock.

The other three scorpion species that occur on Table Mountain all belong to the more venomous family Buthidae. These are much smaller scorpions, with feeble pincers but thick tails, as they subdue their prey by stinging it. The most common is *Uroplectes lineatus*, which is tolerant of a wide variety of habitats and lives in shallow scrapes under rocks or beneath the bark of trees. The two remaining species have narrower distribution ranges. *Uroplectes variegatus* occurs in dry fynbos on the western slopes of the mountain, while the endemic Table Mountain scorpion *Uroplectes insignis* is restricted to the wet, eastern slopes.

## THE PROVIDERS

Female hunting wasps appear to be completely devoted mothers, intent on providing for the needs of their developing offspring. Most make their nests underground, a challenging undertaking in Table Mountain's loose quartzitic sands. Fortunately for the naturalist, some of the best places to search for hunting wasps are along paths, where the soil has become compacted enough for nest construction.

During the hot summer months, the female sand wasp *Ammophila ferrugineipes* can be seen digging in sandy ground on Table Mountain (*Ammophila* means "sand lover"). She removes pellets of sand and small stones in her jaws and deposits them up to 30 centimetres from the work site, so that no heap of sand betrays the presence of the nest. Gradually she constructs a vertical tunnel about 10 millimetres wide and 80 millimetres deep, leading to a small chamber that serves as a nursery for her young. Once satisfied with her handiwork she sets off on a hunting mission, scurrying over bushes and frequently inspecting the undersides of leaves for the small green "looper" or "inchworm" caterpillars belonging to the moth family Geometridae. Sometimes fresh faecal pellets on the ground give away a caterpillar in the leaves above. As soon as one is found, the wasp stings it in several places, injecting a venom which induces a

*1 With tail cocked for action, a Cape burrowing scorpion* Opistophthalmus capensis *faces its assailant with poison tip at the ready. Despite their fierce appearance, burrowing scorpions are not very venomous and instead rely on their powerful pincers to subdue prey.*
*2 Sac spiders* Clubiona *do not spin webs to catch prey, but rather ambush other spiders and small insects.*

1

2

# Parasites of acraea butterflies

The garden acraea *Acraea horta* is one of the most familiar butterflies to the residents of Cape Town, yet those that are seen fluttering lazily about represent the few fortunate survivors of an annual genocide.

Caterpillars of the garden acraea feed on the leaves of the wild peach tree *Kiggelaria africana*, which is abundant both in the forests on the lower slopes of Table Mountain and in suburban gardens. From the moment they hatch, the caterpillars are vulnerable to parasitism by a succession of enemies. Initially they are targeted by the braconid wasp *Apantales acraea*, which injects its eggs into the caterpillars with a needle-like ovipositor. As soon as the wasp larvae hatch they begin feeding on the internal organs of their hosts. This causes a change in the behaviour of the parasitised caterpillars and many of them crawl away from the tree, but all finally succumb to the parasites. Then the *Apantales* wasp larvae emerge from the decimated corpses and each spins a small white cocoon in which it will complete its metamorphosis.

Older caterpillars that were lucky enough to escape the *Apantales* wasps face a second onslaught, this time from an ichneumonid wasp such as one of the *Charops* species. As before, the wasp injects an egg into the caterpillar and the grub that hatches devours its host from the inside out, causing it to shrivel and die. The mottled grey and black cocoon of the ichneumonid wasp is easy to recognise as it hangs from a leaf by a silken thread. In a strange twist of fate, the pupae of the ichneumonid wasp may themselves fall victim to other parasites, a phenomenon known as hyperparasitism.

Acraea caterpillars that survive to reach maturity typically leave the tree and pupate on a rock or the trunk of another tree. Even as pupae they are not safe from parasites and are frequently attacked by a stout chalcid wasp, *Brachymeria kassalensis*. In trying to defend themselves the pupae thrash about wildly, but the wasps are persistent and eventually manage to inject an egg into each. The *Brachymeria* larvae develop rapidly and within weeks they have devoured the pupae and grown into adult wasps. The males emerge first and begin

searching for females, which are still inside the pupae. After a male has located a female by smell, he hovers around her pupa, waiting for the first sign of her – a pair of jaws snipping away at the shell – and sometimes mates with her even before she has fully emerged. Once impregnated, the female goes off in search of other pupae in which to lay her eggs, continuing the cycle of parasitism of the unfortunate garden acraea.

Parasites play an important role in limiting the abundance of insects, and are believed to cause the yearly fluctuations in abundance so typical of butterflies. For example, in "good" butterfly years, such as 1994 in Cape Town, the population of acraea butterflies reaches a peak, which in turn leads to a great increase in the numbers of parasites. This means that nearly all of the butterflies are parasitised and killed during the following year; indeed, during 1996 and 1997 it was difficult to find acraea butterflies in Cape Town. The parasite population subsequently also crashes in the absence of sufficient hosts, allowing the butterfly population to start gradually building up again, ready for a repeat of the whole cycle.

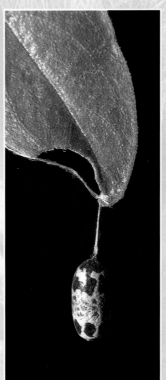

**1** *An ichneumonid wasp* Charops *stabs at the side of a young caterpillar, injecting a single egg. When it hatches the grub will slowly devour the caterpillar from the inside out.*

**2** *The pupal case of* Charops *is attached to leaves by a silken thread. At this stage of its life cycle the parasitic wasp is vulnerable to attack by other parasites, in a phenomenon known as hyperparasitism.*

**3** *A suitor waits for a female chalcid wasp* Brachymeria kassalensis *to emerge from the pupal case of an acraea caterpillar. As soon as she has been impregnated, she will go in search of other pupae in which to lay her eggs.*

**4** *The pupal case of the braconid wasp* Apantales acraea *has an outer layer of silk that probably serves as physical protection from other parasites.*

**1** A female sand wasp Ammophila ferrugineipes takes food to her developing young.
**2** A Hemipepsis spider-hunting wasp drags a paralysed rain spider to her nest, while a parasitic tachinid fly rides piggyback.
**3** Returning from a successful hunt, a female Bembix sibilans wasp removes a thin layer of sand and enters her nest with a freshly killed fly.

**4** Warning colours and a coat of bristles do not protect a lappet moth caterpillar Pachypasa capensis from parasitic braconid wasp larvae, here bursting from its body to spin their silken cocoons.
**5** The cuckoo wasp Chrysis lays its eggs in paralysed caterpillars inside the nests of mud wasps. Its larvae will eat both the host larvae and their food supply.

deep state of paralysis. Then she tucks the caterpillar firmly under her body and flies back to the nest, where she dumps it unceremoniously at the entrance. She leaves it for a moment while she inspects the interior, before reaching out and dragging the caterpillar into the hole. After laying an egg in it she goes in search of a small stone to block the entrance to the nest, trying out various sizes until she finds the best fit.

The female *Ammophila ferrugineipes* is a hardworking parent and provides a constant supply of food for her young. She spends each night hanging from a nearby branch by her jaws, exposed to the elements, while they lie comfortably ensconced in their nest. Every morning she sets off hunting, and each time a paralysed caterpillar has been deposited in the nest she carefully places the stone back over the entrance. The last time she leaves the nest she partially fills the burrow with debris, replaces the stone, and then sweeps sand over the entrance, removing all clues to its whereabouts. Sometimes she even goes as far as placing small twigs over the nest entrance. The larvae are then left to pupate, safe in the sealed nest for the winter.

Spider-hunting wasps are possibly the most formidable insect hunters on the mountain, and their noisy, agitated flight gives the impression of an irascible temperament. These very large orange and black wasps, some as long as 50 millimetres, belong to the genus *Hemipepsis*. They are sometimes seen running rapidly over the ground in search of their preferred prey, the large ground spiders *Palystes*. When they find one the attack is swift and deadly. The victim is stung repeatedly, and paralysis quickly sets in as the venom takes effect. The spider is then dragged to a suitable crack or crevice, where an egg is laid in it before it is covered over with sand and debris.

Male spider-hunting wasps do not indulge in this macabre behaviour; on Table Mountain they are pollinators of the orchid *Disa bivalvata*, which attracts them by mimicking the sex pheromones produced by the female wasps.

Sandy embankments on Table Mountain are the favourite nesting sites for the fly-hunting wasp *Bembix sibilans*, which lives in small colonies. The female works at a frenetic pace to construct her nest, raking the sand with the stiff bristles on her front legs. She excavates a small chamber about 5 to 10 centimetres below the ground, in which she lays a single egg. Once it has hatched the growing larva is constantly supplied with freshly caught flies, and each time the female departs she carefully sweeps sand over the nest's entrance to reduce the chances that the larva will be discovered by parasitic milto-grammine flies. If the larva survives the high-risk period during its first two weeks of life, it spins a compact cocoon in which it will spend the winter.

Bee pirates are solitary wasps related to *Bembix* which specialise in hunting honeybees. There are two species on Table Mountain. The banded bee pirate *Palarus latifrons* waits at the hive and catches worker honeybees in flight, but the more frequently observed species is the yellow bee pirate *Philanthus triangulum*, which ambushes honey-bees at flowers. As in *Bembix*, the females construct a short sloping tunnel for a nest and bring freshly killed or paralysed bees to the growing larvae on a daily basis.

Among the most beautiful insects on Table Mountain are the cuckoo wasps, which belong to the genus *Chrysis*. They have metallic green, purple or multi-hued bodies that glitter brightly in the sun. Their lifestyle emulates that of the bird of the same name, in that they lay their eggs in the nests of other species. They are quite specific in their choice of host, and as soon as the cuckoo wasp grub hatches it uses its powerful jaws to kill and feed on the host grub.

## THE TRAPPERS

Apart from its many and varied rapacious insects, Table Mountain also has a rich and interesting fauna of spiders, which excel in ingenious methods of prey capture.

The brightly coloured orb web spiders on Table Mountain, belonging to the genus *Argiope*, spin impressive silk webs which can be more than a metre in diameter. Most of the spiders have several types of silk glands, each used for a different pur-pose. Any small insect trapped in the main web is quickly wrapped in a fine sheet of silk, and only once it is firmly bound in this straitjacket does the spider inject its venom. The victim is then left hanging on the web, like meat at the butcher's, to be eaten at the spider's leisure. The most common prey of orb web spiders are grasshoppers, which are quickly subdued before their powerful legs destroy the finely crafted web.

**6** *A small grasshopper is expertly wrapped in silk before being injected with venom by an* Argiope *orb web spider.*
**7** *Dew clinging to an orb web reveals its intricate design.*

6

7

The black baboon spider *Harpactira baviana* spins a web across the entrance to its underground burrow, and any insect unfortunate enough to stumble into it is rapidly impaled by the spider's large fangs. When threatened out in the open, baboon spiders put on a defensive display, holding up their front legs and revealing a bright red area around their mouthparts.

The stone nest spider *Nemoscoles* protects itself from predators by constructing a nest of small stones, secured with silk and suspended above the ground by a silken girdle. The spider shelters in the nest until an insect is caught in the small conical web hanging below, and then emerges cautiously before rushing out to bite and poison the prey. As it is vulnerable to attack if it eats its meal out in the open, the spider attaches a thread to the prey and frees it from the web. It then retreats back to the nest and hauls in its victim, tugging at the thread in a hand-over-hand fashion, so that its meal can be eaten at leisure.

*OPPOSITE*: *Communal spiders* Stegodyphus dumicola *immobilise a trapped grasshopper.*
**1** *The baboon spider* Harpactira baviana *traps or ambushes prey from silk-lined, underground burrows.*

1

# Net-casting spider

A crowd favourite during the games of Roman times was the retiarius, a gladiator with a net that was hurled over the opponent. Long before the Romans invented the game there were spiders which had perfected the art of throwing nets over their prey. These net-casting spiders, belonging to the family Deinopidae, are seldom seen by the public as they are strictly nocturnal hunters.

In 1904 the zoologist W.F. Purcell described a spider that he had found on the Cape Peninsula and in nearby Betty's Bay. He named it the camel-back spider *Avellopsis capensis*, having no idea of its net-casting abilities. The species was not seen again until 1991, when it was rediscovered by Norman Larsen, an amateur arachnologist. While walking in Newlands Forest, Larsen found a small piece of web that he guessed must have been made by one of the net-casting spiders. Armed with a flashlight, he returned to the forest with a companion

*A camel-back spider* Avellopsis capensis *hangs poised with its cast net, ready to throw it over passing prey. The spider spins a new cast net each evening and eats it just before daybreak – a good example of recycling in nature.*

that night, and they located their first *Avellopsis* just a few metres from where the web had earlier been found.

Larsen recently accompanied us to Newlands Forest to show us a colony of *Avellopsis* that he has been studying since then. We arrived at the site after dark, but had no problem finding the spiders as Larsen seemed to know the exact locality of each individual. We watched the spiders in action, and studied their technique. Each spider hangs head-down above a leaf with its net held in its two front pairs of legs. A few silk strands stretched between the spider and the leaf transmit vibrations as the prey approaches. This is the signal for the spider to lunge forward, opening its front legs so that the net spreads out. The net is not actually released during the "cast", but it is constructed of such sticky silk that it binds to the prey. The problem of what to do with the net in the morning has an elegant solution – the spider simply eats it.

# Life in a restio tussock

Restios, or Cape reeds, are some of the most distinctive plants of Table Mountain. In areas of waterlogged or shallow soil, such as the upper plateau, a variety of restios grow together in almost continuous fields. Living among the swaying green stalks is a community of animals uniquely adapted for hunting and hiding.

Hiding is much easier in a bush than in a restio tussock, where any animal is likely to stand out as a big, dark bump on the perfectly smooth and green surface of a restio stalk. The solution for several animals is to take on the guise of the scale-like brown bracts that project from the restio stalks at regular intervals. Restio hoppers, which suck the sap from the stalks, are the masters of this disguise. Their forewings have the same colour and texture as a restio bract, and their gradually tapering bodies culminate in a long, cone-shaped snout, mimicking the shape of the restio bract. A scattering of minute, pale dots, resembling the stomata of the restio, adds a finishing touch.

Restio hoppers rely so much on their disguise as a means of defence that they have become poor jumpers, and cannot nearly rival the spectacular leaps of other leaf hoppers. Furthermore, all of the males and most of the females have lost their hind wings and are unable to fly. The few females that are winged are the individuals that disperse to new habitats, so they have shorter snouts and better developed eyes to improve their flying ability.

Long-snouted restio hoppers belong to the tribe Cephalelini, which only occurs in South Africa, Australia and New Zealand, matching the distribution of restios. There are many species of restio hoppers on the Cape Peninsula, but one, *Cephalelus ivyae*, which lives in *Restio tetragonus* tussocks at Scarborough, is thought to be endemic.

Some spiders, such as species of rain spiders *Palystes* and bark spiders *Caerostris*, are too large to attempt restio bract mimicry, and opt instead to conceal themselves in restio inflorescences. Restios of the genera *Hypodiscus* and *Willdenowia* produce a single large nut on the end of the stalk, which is held in a basket of stiff bracts. After the nut is released, the empty basket is an ideal shelter for spiders.

The rain spider builds a secure nest for its eggs and young by binding together a tube of restio stalks with silk. If chased from its nest, the spider does not try to hide itself on the ground, but runs up to the most exposed position, and with legs curled into a tight bunch, hides in the basket of bracts at the tip of the restio. Here the patterning on its abdomen renders it almost invisible.

**1** An apparently lifeless field of restios on the mountain's Back Table crawls with hidden life.
**2** A neddicky *Cisticola fulvicapilla* searches for insects among the restios.
**3** Long-snouted restio hoppers *Cephalelus* are camouflaged as restio bracts to reduce the risk of detection by predators.
**4** A spider protects its eggs inside a silk-lined tube of restio stalks.

**1** A female rain spider Palystes castaneus puts on a threatening display as she guards her nest.
**2** Apart from having a fiercely protective mother, young Palystes spiders are safe from birds and spider-hunting wasps inside an almost impenetrable nest of silk and dried leaves.
**3** Curled snugly against the stem of a burnt protea bush, this Caerostris bark spider is almost perfectly camouflaged.
**4** Despite their cryptic appearance, stick insects are often spotted by birds and are a favourite food item. They are active mainly at night, when they feed on succulent plant parts.
**5** A grasshopper blends into the background of coarse-grained sand on Table Mountain.

Female spiders are usually actively involved in the care of their young. Rain spiders of the genus *Palystes* build leaves and twigs into their nests, probably to protect their offspring from predators such as wasps and birds. These "bag of leaves" nests, bound together with silk and about the size of a tennis ball, are often found suspended from the branches of a shrub. While the young spiderlings live in the nest they are guarded by their mother, but once they have dispersed she resumes her free-ranging lifestyle, hunting at night without using webs to catch prey.

## HIDING

The ability to conceal themselves is highly beneficial to animals that ambush their prey, but concealment is also advantageous to prey, especially when the predator has a keen pair of eyes. Insects, in particular, are masters of camouflage and many take on the appearance of sticks, stones, bark or leaves. Most camouflaged insects move slowly or remain still for long periods, as any sudden movement would betray their presence. For example, stick insects have little defence against predators other than their ability to remain undetected in the foliage, so they feed mainly at night and remain motionless during the day. Even so, many birds still find and eat these tasty morsels. When handled, stick insects may put on a threatening display as a last resort, lifting their front legs to reveal two bright red patches.

The early larval stages of the citrus swallowtail *Papilio demodocus* resemble bird droppings, but when they grow too large for this deception to be convincing, they become green and camouflaged. On Table Mountain the main host plant for these caterpillars is the blister bush *Peucedanum galbanum*, which has divided leaves, so caterpillars feeding on them tend to have a variegated pattern for effective camouflage. Those feeding on common garden citrus plants, however, are more likely to have a plain green coloration to escape detection by predators.

*1 A mosaic of coloured scales on a caterpillar of the pine emperor moth* Imbrasia cytherea *acts as a warning to would-be predators to leave it alone.*
*2 These mating pyrgomorphid grasshoppers are confident that they will not be disturbed as their lurid colours warn birds and baboons that they are toxic.*
*3 Using surprise to get the upper hand,* Cassionympha cassius *displays its eyespots to startle insectivorous birds.*
*4 Blister beetles contain cantharadin toxins for self-defence, hence their bold warning coloration.*

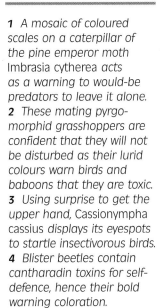

Some spiders are also camouflaged to resemble twigs or bits of bark to reduce their chances of being noticed by predatory birds. The bark spider *Caerostris* is passed unnoticed by most walkers on Table Mountain. It spins large webs between shrubs, but when threatened it flees across to a branch and lies flat against the bark.

Eyespots are another means of deception used mainly by caterpillars, moths and butterflies, such as the mountain pride *Aeropetes tulbaghia*, autumn brown *Dira clytus*, pine emperor *Imbrasia cytherea* and the hawkmoth caterpillar *Hippotion eson*. Eyespots not only startle would-be predators if they are suddenly exposed, but may also divert attention away from the vulnerable and more vital fleshy parts of the body.

## CHEMICAL DEFENCE

Instead of hiding, some animals seem almost to flaunt themselves in front of predators, making no effort to flee when approached. These animals are usually protected with noxious and foul-tasting chemicals, and have bright colours to warn predators to leave them alone. Inexperienced predators that do sample them quickly learn to associate the colours with poisonous fare.

Bright red and black pyrgomorphid grasshoppers are among the most conspicuous insects on Table Mountain. They are able to feed lazily on leaves because they have few enemies, thanks to a foul-smelling and poisonous glandular secretion. The equally gaudy blister beetles *Mylabris* produce a toxin known as cantharadin that oozes from their

5

joints when they are attacked. Cantharadin can kill an adult human after ingestion of just a few milligrams, and on contact with the skin it causes a severe blistering reaction, hence the common name of these insects. Incredibly, the toxin is the main ingredient of the aphrodisiac known as "Spanish fly", which acts by inflaming the sex organs. A concoction made from powdered blister beetles was reputed to have been a key ingredient of Roman orgies!

The large bombardier beetles *Thermophilum decemguttatum* that are often seen scuttling across bare patches of ground on the mountain have one of the most sophisticated kinds of chemical defence – the insect equivalent of a mace spray! When attacked they explosively discharge an acidic mixture from their anus that burns the skin and eyes on contact.

Tiger moths of the genus *Rhodogastria* defend themselves with a foul-smelling froth produced by glands on the thorax. Once the danger has passed, the froth is imbibed through the proboscis to conserve body fluid.

The caterpillars of moths and butterflies are especially vulnerable to being eaten, since they lack the tough exoskeleton that provides the first line of defence for most adult insects. Bagworms, the caterpillars of the moth family Psychidae, make up for this by enclosing themselves in a protective casing of twigs bound together with silk. Many other species protect themselves with hairs, which hamper parasitic wasps in their quest

to inject their eggs, or spines, which not only spike predators but may ooze poisonous liquids when broken.

In fact, many caterpillars have evolved some form of chemical defence. Poisonous caterpillars, such as those of the African monarch *Danaus chrysippus*, have bright warning colours and are left alone by birds and lizards. The remarkable manner in which some caterpillars obtain poisons from their food plants is described in the previous chapter.

One of the most unusual forms of defence against predators is found in the larva of the citrus swallowtail *Papilio demodocus*, which uses shock tactics when attacked. A lurid orange tentacle, or osmeterium, forked like a snake's tongue and usually concealed in a pouch behind the head, is thrust out when danger threatens. It is accompanied by the release of a pungent liquid that smells like rotten pineapple (probably a by-product of the oil-rich leaves consumed by the caterpillars), and the combined effect is enough to frighten away most predators.

No form of defence against predators is perfect, and even the most camouflaged, spiny and poisonous animals regularly fall prey to other animals. This never-ending struggle for survival is the catalyst for further evolution, and natural history is enriched as a result.

**5** *The gaudy colours of these mating window-winged moths* Syntomis cerbera *signal to birds that they are distasteful and poisonous insects.*
**6** *Striking a defensive pose, a caterpillar of the citrus swallowtail butterfly* Papilio demodocus *extrudes a pair of bright, horn-like tentacles from behind its head, accompanied by the release of a pungent odour.*

6

# Life in the Shadows

Leaving the fynbos behind and entering the cool, dark forest is like stepping into a different world. Trees tower overhead, their branches closing into a protective canopy that shuts out sun, wind and noise. A rich smell of humus hangs in the air, and dead leaves rustle underfoot.

Forests come nowhere near matching the staggering diversity of plants in the fynbos. On the Cape Peninsula there are only 33 species of forest tree, yet identifying even these few species is difficult, as their leaves and fruit are often out of reach and flowers are seldom present.

The bastard saffronwood *Cassine peragua* is one of the easiest to recognise, as its trunk is irregular and fluted and covered with orange bark. When held up to the light, a network of yellow veins can be seen in its leaves. Often found growing nearby is the hard pear *Olinia ventosa*, one of the largest trees in the forest. Its bark is fissured into small rectangular blocks that peel up at the ends, and its leaves emit a strong smell of almonds when crushed.

The silky bark *Maytenus acuminata* has leaves that produce latex threads when they are folded and then pulled in two. The only other tree with this characteristic is the white silky bark *Cassine eucleiformis*, which on the Cape Peninsula occurs only in Orange Kloof. Another locally rare forest tree is the white stinkwood *Celtis africana*, identified by its smooth white trunk and asymmetrical leaf veins.

No forest is complete without lianas, or monkey ropes, and two large species commonly occur on the Cape Peninsula. Melktou *Secamone alpini* is one of the milkweeds (Asclepiadaceae), its leaves exuding the family's characteristic milky white sap when torn. The seed pods split open to release tufted white seeds which parachute into forest clearings, where opportunities for growth are most favourable. The other large liana is the forest grape *Rhoicissus tomentosa*, which relies on birds to disperse its succulent black fruit. Like its relative the grapevine, the leaves turn scarlet before they drop.

Few plants are able to survive in the shady conditions beneath the forest canopy. The most common understorey plants are ferns, particularly the five members of the genus *Blechnum*, which can form dense thickets in wet areas, and the sword sedge *Schoenoxiphium lanceum*, which has sharp-edged leaves that make barefoot walking unpleasant in places. Another typical understorey plant is *Knowltonia vesicatoria*, a member of the ranunculus family that has three-lobed, plasticky leaves and a large bulb that is often collected for its purported medicinal properties.

OPPOSITE: *Forests are a world apart from fynbos, and governed by totally different ecological rules. Here light is a limiting resource and competition for it promotes the growth of tall trees.*
**1** *The abundance of bird-dispersed fruits, such as those of the wild peach* Kiggelaria africana, *sets forest apart from fynbos, where seeds are typically transported by wind or ants.*
**2** *Catching a passing ray of light, a creeping fern* Elaphoglossum acrostichoides *is one of the few plants able to survive in the deep shade under the forest canopy.*
**3** *Flowering from its bare trunk, a tree-fuchsia* Halleria lucida *improves its chances of attracting first pollinating sunbirds and then fruit-eating birds.*

1

2

*After tumbling down from the cliffs above, boulders soon become colonised by mosses (1) and liverworts (2) in the damp, shaded environment of the forest.*

## FORESTS PAST AND PRESENT

An aerial view of Table Mountain shows the forests as a scattering of dark-green patches against a backdrop of grey fynbos. On the dry western and northern slopes these are no more than clumps of trees clustered around scree slopes, or hunkered down in deep kloofs where they are protected from fire. In the wetter southern and eastern areas the forests spill out of the valleys and blanket the slopes above Newlands, Kirstenbosch and Hout Bay. Some species, such as the ironwood *Olea capensis macrocarpa*, stinkwood *Ocotea bullata*, hard pear *Olinia ventosa* and white silky bark *Cassine eucleiformis* only occur in these large, wet forests. Their streams are shaded by the African holly *Ilex mitis* and rooiels *Cunonia capensis*, and, in more open areas, the wild almond *Brabejum stellatifolium*.

On the drier western slopes of the mountain, where the forests overlook the Atlantic Ocean, the Hottentot's cherry *Maurocenia frangula*, the fragrant camphor bush *Tarchonanthus camphoratus*, the wild olive *Olea europea africana* and the coast cabbage tree *Cussonia thyrsiflora*, with its distinctive hand-shaped leaves, are more typical. Closer to the sea, milkwoods *Sideroxylon inerme* dominate the forests, their canopies stunted and smoothed by wind and sea spray. Here only thick-leafed, shade-tolerant plants like the Hottentot's cherry and the pock ironwood *Chionanthus foveolatus* can survive among the gnarled and twisted milkwood trunks.

In most areas milkwood forests have been replaced by coastal housing. At Hout Bay only a small plot of trees has escaped the developer's bulldozer, and it is now a national monument, while at Llandudno the small forest lining the beach is still a pleasure to amble through. Towards the edges of the bay it tapers out into a low thicket of dune saffronwood *Cassine maritima*, sea guarri *Euclea racemosa* and coast olive *Olea exasperata*. This coastal thicket, also called strandveld, lines the undeveloped shores of the Peninsula and extends far along the eastern and western coasts of South Africa, its ecology and species composition sharing many features with forest vegetation.

Most of the large forests on Table Mountain grow on the granite-derived, clay soils of the lower slopes. However, a few forest patches occur on the shallow sandstone soils at higher altitudes, as in Diamond Spring Valley on the Back Table, where an unusual cleft in the mountain provides refuge from wind and fires. At these altitudes moisture from the "tablecloth" encourages the growth of *Usnea* lichens, which hang from the branches in long green beards.

The mountain's forest patches are not the remnants of a once continuous forest fragmented by woodcutting and fire, as is often presumed. When Jan van Riebeeck arrived at the Cape in 1652, he recorded that little timber could be found on the dry north face, and larger forests were to be found only on the eastern slopes of the mountain. Van Riebeeck ordered a wagon road to be cut to this forest, which today is the main road from the Castle to the southern suburbs.

By the time Willem van der Stel arrived at the Cape some three decades later, the mountain's

*The rooiels* Cunonia capensis, *typically found growing alongside streams in the Peninsula forests, has large compound leaves (3) that unfurl from distinctive spoon-shaped buds (4). The family Cunoniaeceae has a southern hemisphere distribution, but other members of the genus* Cunonia, *which contains 15 species, occur only on New Caledonia, an island off the east coast of Australia.*

3

4

# Wild almonds

The first indigenous trees planted by the colonists were not intended for timber or kitchen fires, but as protection from thieves. In 1660 Jan van Riebeeck had the idea of planting a wild almond hedge, extending for 20 kilometres in a half-circle around the colony, to safeguard the livestock from cattle rustlers.

The wild almond tree *Brabejum stellatifolium* branches very close to the ground, while its thick trunks snake along horizontally and twist together to form a tall, dense hedge, so Van Riebeeck was wise in his choice. His men harvested the fruits of the tree in the nearby forests, where they were just starting to ripen in the last rays of the summer sun, and planted them along a strip of ploughed land. Ever since then the hedge has propagated itself, and fragments of it still flourish in Kirstenbosch and in the suburb of Bishopscourt, where it is protected as a national monument.

1

2

3

*An unusual member of the protea family, the wild almond* Brabejum stellatifolium *has flowers (1) resembling those of other proteas, but almond-like fruits (2) that are dispersed by water to the streamside sites it favours (3).*

The fruits of the wild almond contain cyanide, but the Khoi knew how to detoxify them by bleaching, leaching and roasting, and they formed an important part of their diet. Van Riebeeck thought that the treated fruits would make good pig food, but when one of his men died after trying the brew, he quickly abandoned the idea.

forests had been so decimated that building operations had to be halted because there was not enough wood to repair wheelbarrows. The forests in Hout Bay were relatively protected as they were only accessible by boat.

These historical accounts suggest that the forests on the eastern and southern slopes of Table Mountain were at one time at least twice as extensive as they are today, but even then there were only small patches of forest on the drier northern and western slopes.

*1  Married into an inextric-able relationship of mutual benefit, nutrient-absorbing fungal threads and photo-synthetic algal cells together make up the body of this* Cladonia *lichen. The red spore-bearing structures give the species its common name, British soldiers.*
*2  At high altitude, moisture condensing from mist and clouds encourages the growth of* Usnea *lichens, known as old man's beard.*
*3  Mist descends on a forest on Table Mountain, bringing cool and damp conditions.*

## THE FOREST ARCHIPELAGO

By African standards, the forests on Table Mountain grow in a cool environment, 4 000 kilometres from the equator and surrounded by a cold ocean. In the tropical and inland areas of Africa, such cool environments are found only at very high altitudes. Mountain peaks, plateaus and extinct volcanoes form an archipelago of cool habitats throughout the continent, and the forests that grow on these widely separated habitat islands have many species in common with Table Mountain's forests. African holly *Ilex mitis*, Cape beech *Rapanea melano-phloeos* and white pear *Apodytes dimidiata*, for example, occur in almost all of them.

These afromontane forests differ in several respects from Africa's hot, tropical forests, such as those in the Congo basin and Maputaland. For a start, trees in afromontane forests do not grow very tall, so they do not need the support of buttress roots. They also grow slowly, so they have hard, durable leaves that can stay on the tree for a number of years before needing replacement. The cool conditions favour naturally slow-growing plants such as yellowwoods and tree ferns, and exclude fast-growing and light-demanding trees such as members of the pea family, which often dominate forests in warmer areas.

Nevertheless, climate alone cannot explain the overall similarity of the islands of afromontane forest. How did plants cross the vast tracts of inhospitable habitat separating them?

Two theories have been proposed. The older one contends that the patches are remnants of a continuous belt of forest that covered much of the continent during the last Ice Age 18 000 years ago, before it was fragmented by climate change and human activity. However, recent evidence suggests that the Ice Ages, although cold, were relatively dry – conditions unlikely to have been suitable for extensive forests.

The more recent theory is that seed-dispersal by birds, migrating over long distances, allowed forest

*4  A typical member of the Peninsula's drier, sea-facing forests, a coast cabbage tree* Cussonia thyrsiflora *is easily identified by its hand-shaped leaves. It usually depends on neighbouring plants to support its limp and sprawling branches.*

*5  The moist forest of the eastern and southern slopes of Table Mountain has a dense understorey of ferns, such as this* Pteris dentata, *one of 24 species of forest fern on the Peninsula.*

*6  Like the flora, the birdlife in forests has little in common with fynbos. Here fruit-eating birds and flycatchers predominate, while the predatory niche is filled by specialist forest hunters such as this wood owl* Strix woodfordii.

plants to spread from one patch to another. According to this view the afromontane forest patches were never much larger than they are today, and might even have been smaller or fewer. This scenario is supported by fossil pollen studies, which have revealed that mud deposited during the last Ice Age contained only small amounts of pollen from forest plants, yet plenty from grasses and other open country species.

In solving this riddle, it is also important to consider the distribution of forest animals. While the afromontane forests have few endemic trees, they are rich in endemic animals, most of them small and flightless. Unlike the forest trees, which maintain genetic contact through seed dispersal, these small invertebrates are genetically isolated in their forest islands and over time have become endemic species. However, there are some species that contradict this scenario, so the pattern is far from clear and the debate rages on.

Although many afromontane forest plants have a wide distribution, some have a more limited range. For example, the spoonwood *Hartogiella schinoides*, the Hottentot's cherry *Maurocenia frangula* as well as the wild almond *Brabejum stellatifolium*, an unusual member of the protea family, are all restricted to the Cape. These trees may be relics from the ancient period long before the Ice Ages, when forests dominated the Cape.

Another group of forest plants has a distribution range extending along the eastern seaboard to the warm, coastal forests of Maputaland, where they presumably originated. On the Cape Peninsula, these trees, which include the milkwood, tend to grow in warmer areas along the coast.

## THE SEED COURIERS

A loud flapping of wings, breaking the silence of the forest, betrays the presence of a flock of rameron pigeons *Columba arquatrix* in the canopy above. These birds are first-rate seed couriers, as their digestive system only strips the flesh from the seed without harming the delicate embryo inside. In fact, the seeds of some trees, such as the bastard saffronwood *Cassine peragua* and ironwood *Olea capensis macrocarpa*, germinate more quickly if they have passed through the gut of a pigeon.

The seeds are widely dispersed by the birds as they fly as far as 20 kilometres from their roosts each day, while seasonal migrations take them even further afield. Many forest trees do not fruit every year, which means that the pigeons have to fly long distances on sporadic migrations, tracking the availability of their favourite fruit. Ironically, the efficiency of rameron pigeons as long-distance seed dispersers is most evident from the spread of the South American bugweed *Solanum mauritianum*,

# Magical mushrooms

The countless tales attributing the magical appearance of mushrooms to fairies, witches, lightning and dark forces of every kind have persisted for thousands of years. As if out of nowhere they suddenly materialise, glistening with drops of morning dew. To the naked eye, mushrooms have no roots and produce no seeds, but with the aid of a microscope, samples of the soil or wood on which they grow are seen to be totally invaded by a reticulating network of thin white threads. This is the mycelium, or body, of the fungus, which also serves as its "roots". Unseen from the surface, it might extend throughout the damp leaf litter of a patch of forest.

Unlike plants, fungi do not have the ability to manufacture food from the sun's energy. Instead the mycelium extracts all its nourishment from the wood, animal tissue or humus around it, and when conditions are right and food is plentiful it produces a fruiting body, the mushroom. Its "seeds" are too small to see; they are single-celled spores that drop from the paper-thin divisions under the mushroom cap in their billions.

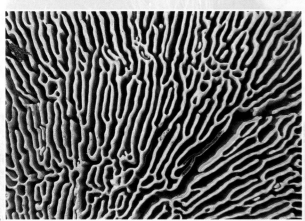

**6** *Bracket fungi play a vital role as decomposers in the forest, unlocking the nutrients bound up in tall trees after they have fallen and died.*

*1 Mushrooms and other fungi are an important source of food for forest animals, such as this inquisitive snail.*

*2 Laetiporus sulphureus is known as the chicken of the woods, because its edible flesh tastes like chicken breast.*

*3 The fly agaric Amanita muscaria has potent toxins that have a hallucinogenic effect on human consumers.*

*4 By taking on the appearance and smell of rotting meat, Clathrus archeri attracts carrion flies that feed on its black sugarcoated spores and disperse them in their faeces.*

*5 The maze of gills on the underside of a bracket fungus releases thousands of tiny spores, but only a small number will find suitable sites for germination.*

which now displays its plump yellow fruits in almost every forest visited by the birds, including those on Table Mountain.

At sunset, small groups of rameron pigeons can be seen flying high overhead as they return to their favourite roosts, deep in the forests on the mountain's eastern slopes. Here their low-pitched, cooing call is often heard resonating through the forest, but only early risers will be able to eavesdrop on the male's courtship routine, when he spirals down to the canopy on stiff wings to the accompaniment of a loud nasal bleating.

The call of the sombre bulbul *Andropadus importunus* is one of the most distinctive sounds of the forests on Table Mountain, but the bird is not often seen among the tangled vegetation that it favours. Ironically, fruit-eaters like the bulbul are frequently not as effective at seed dispersal as omnivorous birds such as the olive thrush *Turdus olivaceus* and the Cape white-eye *Zosterops pallidus*, which venture more widely in search of insects.

At night, Egyptian fruit bats *Rousettus aegyptiacus* take over the fruit-eating niche in the forests on Table Mountain, harvesting the riches of the bastard saffronwood *Cassine peragua*, turkey berry *Canthium inerme* and bladder-nut *Diospyros whyteana*. A tree with a large crop of fruit will attract many bats, circling on silent wings. Occasionally a bat will swoop into the canopy of the tree, land near the fruit and clamber about, sniffing audibly, until it finds one that is ripe. Small fruits are usually eaten on site, but larger ones are carried off in the mouth to a convenient perch some distance away. There the bats hang by one foot while manipulating the fruit into the mouth with the other. Once the fruit is inside the bulging cheek pouches, the flexible lips make a tight seal. With a quick chomp or two the hard seed is separated from the flesh and dropped out of the corner of the mouth, and the fruit is then squeezed between the tongue and the palate until it is reduced to a dry pellet of fibres and husk. Only the fruit juice is swallowed, while the dry pellets collect in piles under favourite perches. Feeding frenzies are always a noisy business, with much squealing over stolen and dropped fruit.

**GROWING UP IN A FOREST**

The interlocking pattern of the forest canopy's leaves and branches, so effective at shutting out the sun, is the result of constant competition among trees for access to light. In the race towards the sun, trees grow taller and taller, and put out branches to fill every gap with leaves so that they can soak up the energy-rich rays. But the shady conditions under the canopy are not at all conducive to rapid seedling growth, and this is the key to forest ecology.

In some parts of the forest, the seedlings of the ironwood *Olea capensis macrocarpa* and the Cape beech *Rapanea melanophloeos* wait in dense banks in the forest understorey. Though they are

*Making full use of its moment of sunlight, a young turkey berry* Canthium inerme *(1) cranes up towards the distant canopy, but it will be many years before it achieves its goal. Lianas, such as the forest grape* Rhoicissus tomentosa *(2), take a faster route, snaking up the trunks of mature trees and soon bursting through into the sunshine. The forest grape uses birds to disperse its seeds, attracting them with juicy black berries, while the other large forest liana, the melktou* Secamone alpini *(3), has tufted, wind-dispersed seeds.*

1

2

3

4

small, these seedlings are probably much older than they look, for in the half-light of the forest they remain in a state of suspended growth, producing only enough food to stay alive. Their durable leaves require little maintenance and seldom need to be replaced.

Occasionally one of the canopy trees loses a branch or dies, dropping its leaves. The seedlings briefly awaken from their long slumber and stretch up towards the window of light, but the branches of the surrounding trees are already reaching in to close the gap. A seedling will probably need several such boosts of light before it reaches the canopy, so it takes decades for slow-growing species such as yellowwoods to get there.

Not all seedlings are able to play this waiting game. Those of thin-leafed plants such as keurboom *Virgilia oroboides*, rooiels *Cunonia capensis* and wild peach *Kiggelaria africana* are adapted for rapid growth, so they require plenty of sunshine.

Although the adult trees occur inside mature forests, their seedlings are not found on the forest floor. These species are forest pioneers, with seedlings adept at colonising open areas such as the old fynbos in Orange Kloof. If they are not destroyed by fire they might grow into a new forest, attracting birds that bring with them the seeds of shade-requiring forest specialists such as ironwood, stinkwood, hard pear, yellowwood and assegaai *Curtisia dentata*, all of which are rare in the Peninsula's small forests.

Lianas also spread their leaves in the forest canopy, but manage to do so without spending much time as suppressed seedlings in the shade of the understorey. They exploit the competitiveness of forest trees, and use it to their own advantage. After germinating on the forest floor, young lianas coil their lanky bodies around the sturdy trunks of forest trees and snake their way up to the sunlit canopy. They have found a ladder out of the dark prison.

**4** *On warm, windless evenings in spring the forest twinkles with the magical lights of fireflies* Luciola capensis, *flashing for a mate. The predatory larvae of these small beetles live in the forest humus.*

*1 A Peninsula-endemic amphipod,* Talitroides eastwoodae, *lumbers through the forest humus.*
*2 Of the 190 millipede species in South Africa, 155 are restricted to forest habitats, and at least 12 are endemic to the Cape Peninsula.*
*3 Most harvestmen scavenge for dead creatures and fallen fruit on the forest floor, but some capture small prey.*

1

2

3

4

## THE HIDDEN ANIMALS

Inside the forest it is cool and quiet. Leaves spiral down from the canopy intermittently and join the carpet of decomposing plant material on the forest floor. This spongy layer of humus not only nurtures the forest trees with nutrients and water, but also shelters a hidden world, quietly teeming with life. Mites, insect larvae and springtails are most common, but a large proportion of the Peninsula's 100-odd endemic animals also reside here, including harvestmen, sowbugs, amphipods, millipedes, centipedes, primitive flightless insects, earthworms and slugs.

Under their double blanket of forest canopy and humus, these animals live in an environment of constant darkness, temperature and humidity. Such conditions favour primitive animals, which often lack means of resisting desiccation. In the forest humus there is also no need for wings or highly specialised mouthparts, which are typical of modern insects. Here, most animals feed on a simple, low-nutrient diet of rotting plant material and fungi.

In a realm of darkness, surrounded by food, the senses of sight and hearing are also redundant. Instead, the animals of the forest humus explore their kingdom with rows of sensitive bristles, delicate thread-like antennae and quivering mouthparts. Even the business of finding a mate is likely to happen at close range, so there is no need for flashy colours and beautiful songs, and the sexes are generally drab and similar in appearance.

## THE VELVET WORM

Curled up deep inside the protective humus is the most beautiful of all the creatures of the forest floor. Its skin is dark and supple, and covered in millions of microscopic projections, giving it the appearance of black velvet. Against this background the minute eyes sparkle like diamonds, but they serve only to guide the animal away from sunlight. Instead it is the antennae that lead the way, constantly changing shape as they reach out to touch and feel. This is a peripatus, its appearance virtually unchanged since its ancestors inhabited the earth 530 million years ago.

Before the first fishes writhed in ancient seas, peripatusses were feeding in their shallow waters. Then, with remarkably few alterations to their basic design, they moved onto land, and were hiding under logs when the dinosaurs ruled the planet. Like ghost frogs and galaxias fish, the 200 species of modern peripatusses occur only on the continents of the southern hemisphere – testimony to their evolution prior to the break-up of Gondwanaland.

For many years, peripatusses were thought to have played a central role in the evolution of life on earth. They share features with the primitive, segmented worms, such as earthworms and sea-worms, and the more modern arthropods such as insects and millipedes, so they were long considered to be an evolutionary link. However, recent genetic studies suggest that peripatusses are themselves specialised arthropods, rather than arthropod ancestors.

Table Mountain is very unusual in having four species of peripatus occurring together in a small area. *Peripatopsis balfouri,* which has been recorded from the north of the Table Mountain range to as far south as Kalk Bay, is the most common of these, but even it is seldom seen and hard to find. Outside the Peninsula it is widespread in the southwestern Cape, sharing this distribution with *Peripatopsis capensis,* with which it is often found curled up in the same moist hollow.

The other two species are endemic to Table Mountain: *Peripatopsis alba* lives only in the cave system of the Back Table, while *Peripatopsis leonina* was discovered on Signal Hill at the turn of the century. Despite repeated searches we have not been able to find the latter species, and there have been no recorded sightings of it in the last 50 years. Most of its suitable habitat has been lost to alien trees, housing developments and frequent fires, so the Signal Hill peripatus is presumed extinct.

Long pregnancy and live birth is typical of mammals, but incredibly, peripatus has these features too. Some Australian species still lay eggs, but all of the South African ones give birth to perfectly formed, miniature replicas of themselves after a

gestation period of 13 months. Research on their Australian cousins has shown that the female is guided to her mate by following his scent, released from two small glands on his last pair of legs. As the two get acquainted the male deposits glistening sperm packages all over the female's body. Beneath these packages tiny apertures form in her body wall, and the thread-like sperm cells swarm through them in search of the ovaries. A month later, the young of the previous litter have completed their

5          6

**4** *The rare Knysna warbler* Bradypterus sylvaticus *forages on the forest floor by sweeping leaf litter aside with its tail and then turning to snap up the creatures thus revealed.*
**5** *A velvet worm of great distinction, peripatus has been called an evolutionary link and a living fossil.*
**6** *Snuggling together in a moist hollow,* Peripatopsis capensis *curls into a spiral, something that* P. balfouri *never does.*

# W.F. Purcell & R.F. Lawrence

Anyone who is interested in the small animals of forests and caves will soon realise that much of what we know today is built on the work of two great naturalists, William Purcell (1866–1919) and Reginald Lawrence (1897–1987).

Purcell spent his childhood in the unspoilt wilds of a farm called "Bergvliet" at the foot of Table Mountain. Here he developed a love for the small animals of the veld, which in later life would lead him to the formal study of zoology. During his employment at the South African Museum in Cape Town he devoted himself to the study of spiders, scorpions, solifugids and peripatusses. South Africa was still virgin territory for the collector, and Table Mountain was a particularly fruitful hunting ground – every stone hid a treasure-trove of undiscovered zoological jewels.

In a few short years Dr Purcell named almost 300 new species of spiders alone, including the net-casting spider, and described three new species of peripatus, one of them the now extinct Signal Hill peripatus. His detailed and precise descriptions were illustrated with the most meticulous drawings. Yet Dr Purcell's interests were not confined to zoology. During his retire-

*William Frederick Purcell*

S.A. MUSEUM

COURTESY DR HAMISH ROBERTSON

*Mr C. Thorne, Dr R.F. Lawrence and Dr A. Hesse alongside the donkey-drawn wagon that they used on a collecting trip in Kaokaveld in 1925.*

ment, he made an invaluable contribution to our knowledge of the flora of the Cape Peninsula by making an extraordinarily thorough collection of the plants on Bergvliet. Sadly, the Bergvliet farm and its 595 plant species have suffered the same fate that has befallen virtually all of the lowlands around Table Mountain.

Reginald Lawrence followed in Purcell's footsteps, even filling the same post at the South African Museum. His greatest interest was in mites, harvestmen, scorpions, solifugids, millipedes and peripatusses. He wrote more than 200 scientific articles about these animals, and named innumerable new species, including a large proportion of the cave fauna of Table Mountain.

Lawrence was appointed director of the Natal Museum in 1935, but having never enjoyed the slog of administration, resigned from the post in 1948 to study forest animals. This work culminated in the publication of *The Biology of the Cryptic Fauna of Forests*, a wondrous book in which Lawrence weaves the threads of ecology, evolution, physiology and behavioural observations into a holistic natural history of the animals that live in the forest humus.

gestation and are born tail first, just in time for the first winter rains.

When cornered by a predator, such as a spider or a centipede, peripatus puts into action a remarkable defence mechanism. From either side of the head shoot two well-aimed jets of a glandular secretion, which hardens on contact with air, effectively immobilising the enemy.

Peripatus is itself a predator, and captures small animals by sucking onto them with its fleshy lips. Two sets of blade-like teeth slice a hole in the hard shell of the unlucky victim, and the enzyme-laced saliva flows in through this opening and begins digesting the body contents. Before long all that remains of the prey is a few pieces of exoskeleton.

## THE CAVES

The way into Wynberg Cave leads gradually from the shaded environment of the scree forest into the perpetual darkness of the deepest caverns. Inside the cave it is cool, humid and pitch-dark, so it is not surprising that the creatures which live here have much in common with the animals of the forest floor.

Wynberg Cave, and the roughly ten other caves of the Back Table, follow a widening geological fracture that runs east-west along the southern edge of Table Mountain's main sandstone block. Wynberg Cave is the longest of these caves, and Bats' Cave the deepest, dropping to a depth of 50 metres. Further south along the Peninsula there is another extensive cave system in the Kalk Bay mountains. These caves are shallower, and follow horizontal rather than vertical fissures in the rock.

Of the 85 invertebrate species that have been recorded from the caves on the Cape Peninsula, 21 are endemic, and no less than 13 of these are highly specialised cave animals never found in other habitats.

The most common creature that roams the perpetual night of the caves is the cave cricket *Speleiacris tabulae.* Its most striking adaptation is its impressive antennae, which are as thin as hairs and more than twice the length of its body. Like many other cave-inhabiting animals, *Speleiacris* is a Gondwanaland relic, the other members of its tribe occurring in Patagonia, the Falkland Islands, New Zealand and Australia, but not in the drier caves in the rest of South Africa.

A predator of the cave cricket is the pure white cave peripatus *Peripatopsis alba*, which is one of the rarest of all the cave animals on the Cape Peninsula. It has no eyes at all, but its legs are much longer than those of its forest-dwelling relatives. Elongation of appendages is a common theme in cave animals, which use their legs and antennae rather like the blind use a cane.

The streams that flow in the darkness of the caves have a life all their own. Those in the Back Table caves are home to the most exceptional of all Table Mountain's endemic animals, the blind cave shrimp *Spelaeogriphus lepidops*. It spends its life crawling around blindly, nibbling little bits of black detritus that collect in ruts in the stream-bed. Usually its food-filled gut is all that is seen

1 *Shafts of light reach into Vivarium Cave, its humid, dark environment much like that of the forest.*
2 *Table Mountain's unique cave shrimp* Spelaeogriphus lepidops *is a lonely survivor of a family that was quite common millions of years ago. It is blind, having no need of sight in the pitch-darkness of the cave.*
3 *Feeling its way around with hair-like antennae, the endemic cave cricket* Speleiacris tabulae *searches for the fungus-coated bat droppings that are its principal food.*
4 *A harvestman* Speleomontia cavernicola, *one of 21 animals endemic to the caves on Table Mountain, guards its clutch of eggs on the moist roof of Wynberg Cave.*

under torchlight as its body is almost transparent. *Spelaeogriphus* is one of only two living species in the order Spelaeogryphacea, the other occurring in Brazil. These two humble species have a whole branch of the crustacean family tree to themselves!

The most conspicuous and ecologically import-ant members of the cave fauna are bats. In the darkness of the cave, there are no photosynthe-sising plants to produce food, but bats provide the vital link to the sunny world outside when they return to their roosts each sunrise with stomachs full of food. Bat guano and corpses are soon colonised by fungi and bacteria, and become the staple food of the cave crickets and other animals at the bottom of the food chain. Superstitiously regarded as the messengers of the Devil, bats are in fact the deliverers of life-sustaining food for the cave community.

Worldwide, bats can be divided into two very dis-tinct groups: the Megachiroptera, with 163 species, is restricted to the Old World (Europe, Asia, Australia and Africa), while the Microchiroptera, with 814

species, has an almost global distribution. The Megachiroptera (mega-bats) feed on fruit, nectar and pollen, while the Microchiroptera (micro-bats) are largely insectivorous. In total, there are nearly a thousand species of bats, making up one fifth of the mammal species on earth! On Table Mountain the two most common species are Schreiber's long-fingered bat *Miniopterus schreibersii natalensis*, a micro-bat, and the Egyptian fruit bat *Rousettus aegyptiacus*, a mega-bat.

### Schreiber's long-fingered bats

The small, agile bats often seen swooping and darting at sunset could be any of the ten species of insectivorous micro-bats found on Table Mountain, but they are most likely to be Schreiber's long-fingered bats.

In common with other micro-bats, long-fingered bats have pinhead-sized eyes, as they do not rely on vision to hunt or find their way around. Rather, the key to their success is their ability to "see with sound", or echolocate, by emitting high-pitched sounds, out of the hearing range of humans, through their elaborately shaped noses. With their super-sensitive ears, the bats can detect such detail in the returning echoes that they are able to zigzag through dense forests and pluck the smallest insects from the air. If at the last moment the prey is out of reach, the bats use their wings to deflect it into the mouth or scoop it up in the membranous pouch between their legs, so once detected it has little chance of escape. In a single night micro-bats can eat their own body weight in insects, many of them species that are harmful to humans.

In the early hours of the morning the long-fingered bats return to the caves on the mountain, where they hang from the ceiling of the deepest caverns, the sharp claws on their hind feet being able to get a grip on even the smallest projection or crack. They huddle together in tightly packed bunches to minimise their exposed surfaces, thereby reducing heat loss.

When the cold winter comes, life becomes very difficult for micro-bats, because trying to stay warm burns up a lot of food at a time when there are few flying insects around. Some bats migrate to warmer lands, but Schreiber's long-fingered bat opts for hibernation, slowing its metabolism down and living through the winter on stored fat. Its heart rate and temperature drop so low that it may take 20 minutes before the bat is able to move and function normally if it is disturbed. During the waking-up process considerable energy is burned, depleting its precious fat supply.

Hibernation caves are carefully selected, as they must be cold enough to induce a state of torpor. The chilly caves on Table Mountain meet the requirements, and in winter they are dormitories for thousands of sleeping bats, some of them having come from as far as 250 kilometres away.

Just before hibernating the bats mate. The embryo grows a little, but then ceases development until the female bat comes out of hibernation. Four months after development is resumed the young bat is born. The females herd the newborn bats together and surround them with their warm

*An Egyptian fruit bat* Rousettus aegyptiacus *eyes the crop of fruit on a bastard saffronwood* Cassine peragua. *Fruit bats fulfil an important role on Table Mountain, dispersing the fruits of forest trees, while supplying cave animals with a source of food through their guano.*

*1 With a youngster clinging to her side, an Egyptian fruit bat leaves a rowdy bunch on the ceiling of Bats' Cave. Soon the youngster will be too heavy to hitch a ride, and will be left in the cave while its mother goes foraging.*
*2 An apparently lifeless Schreiber's long-fingered bat* Miniopterus schreibersii natalensis *hibernates through the winter months in the quiet depths of Bats' Cave. It will resume activity when warmer weather brings out the flying insects on which it preys.*
*3 Naturally attracted to moist, dark places. Table Mountain ghost frogs* Heleophryne rosei *take up residence in cave entrances, but have to return to sunlit streams to breed.*

bodies, carefully regulating the temperature by huddling closer when necessary.

Schreiber's long-fingered bats are highly successful and widely distributed animals, their range extending throughout Africa, along the southern parts of Europe and Asia, and into the northern parts of Australia.

### Egyptian fruit bats

Even before reaching the entrance to Bats' Cave, one can hear the Egyptian fruit bats squabbling, and smell their musty, fruity aura. Shafts of light filter through the surrounding yellowwood forest and mossy boulders, and fill the first chamber of the cave with an eerie, green glow. Jostled from a favoured position, a bat drops out of the centre of a noisy cluster and spreads its enormous wings, 60 centimetres from tip to tip. At 130 grams, it equals the weight of 13 long-fingered bats.

With big, brown eyes and large dog-like muzzles, mega-bats are aptly called flying foxes. They rely mainly on eyesight to find their way around, so they lack the weird nose and sculptured ears of micro-bats. In fact, the Egyptian fruit bat and its two close relatives are the only flying foxes that have some sonar capability. Theirs is an independently evolved system that is crude in comparison with the specialised nasal structures of micro-bats, the sound simply being made with the tongue and emitted through the corners of the mouth. As the bats investigate a new roost in a cave, strings of rapid

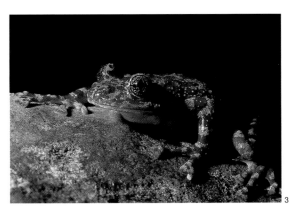

4

clicks are clearly audible to human ears. Other mega-bat species depend on sight alone, and cannot use the dark recesses of caves as daytime refuges. Instead, they roost in trees, sometimes in flocks comprising tens of thousands of individuals.

Although the bats have excellent night vision, it is their sense of smell that guides them to ripe fruit. Their foraging sorties often take them into suburban gardens, where they feast on the fruits of the Outeniqua yellowwood *Afrocarpus fulcatus*, date palms, loquats and figs. This activity has made them very unpopular among some Capetonians because of the spray of bat droppings around their feeding areas, but the gardens may well be providing a substitute for the forested areas that have been lost to development.

In the caves on Table Mountain the fruit bats are sometimes seen with offspring, which cling to their mother's fur and latch onto her nipple with needle-like incisors. When the female goes foraging, the young bat goes along for the ride, and in this way learns which fruits to eat and where to find them. As it grows older it becomes too heavy and has to be left behind in the protected recesses of the cave, but the female soon locates it again on her return, using scent to identify it among the cluster of jostling bats.

Egyptian fruit bats occur from the Cape to Cairo, where the first specimens were collected in the Great Pyramid of Giza. They are absent only from the desert areas of the continent, where fruiting trees are few and far between.

Both Egyptian fruit bats and Schreiber's long-fingered bats need undisturbed, dark caves to survive. If it were not for the caves on Table Mountain, the bats could reach the Peninsula only by commuting across the kilometres of noisy city separating it from the rest of the Cape mountains. By acting as a daytime refuge and hibernation dormitory for bats, Table Mountain's caves play a central role in maintaining essential ecological processes such as seed dispersal and predation, and hence the biodiversity of the Cape Peninsula.

5

*4 Egyptian fruit bats are careful eaters; when feeding on the fruit of a forest tree, such as this bastard saffronwood Cassine peragua, a bat will swallow only the sap and fruit pulp, and drop the seed unharmed from the corner of its mouth.*
*5 Vertical cracks lead down from the broken topography of the Back Table into the cold sandstone heart of the mountain. Caves are the key to the survival of bats on Table Mountain, providing an important day-time refuge, as long as they are left undisturbed.*

# From Source to Sea

High on Table Mountain, a cold mountain stream bubbles and gurgles as it hurtles towards the sea. Clear water glides over a smooth, round boulder, and then dives into a slab of sandstone, momentarily fracturing into a white spray before uniting again in a golden pool. This ever-changing interaction between water and rock creates a diversity of habitats – pool, rapid, backwater and waterfall – each the home of a community of animals adapted to meet the demands of the surrounding micro-environment. But the stream is born long before this, as precipitation in the catchment area.

## MOUNTAIN CATCHMENTS

Most streams on Table Mountain are seasonal, apart from those draining the forested eastern and southern slopes, where a trickle of water can still be found at the height of summer. Catchments on the mountain are typically steep and rocky, so runoff is rapid and there is little retention of rainfall. Within hours of a winter deluge a peaceful mountain stream can become a frothing torrent, and when the rain clouds clear the white streaks of waterfalls can be seen plummeting down the eastern slopes of Devil's Peak, and the precipices above Kirstenbosch.

**OPPOSITE**: *In the dappled shade of Newlands Forest, a stream tumbles over boulders and fallen branches on its journey towards the sea. Hidden beneath the foam, a community of specially adapted animals ekes out a living on leaves that spiral down from the overhanging trees.*
**1** *Ready to grab and devour almost anything that comes its way, a river crab Potamonautes perlatus is a ferocious omnivore.*
**2** *After a winter rainstorm the stream in Skeleton Gorge cascades down the granite ramparts above the contour path, but by the end of summer it is reduced to a mere trickle.*
**3** *Moisture condensing from the "tablecloth" tops up the lakelet near Maclear's Beacon during the drought of summer.*

Streams on the western and northern slopes of the mountain do not have time to develop into rivers before they plunge into the sea. On the western slopes the major stream is Blinkwater, while Platteklip Stream and Silver Stream drain areas of the north face. However, the largest catchment on Table Mountain drains to the south. Much of the water that falls on the plateau collects in a shallow basin in the middle of the mountain, from where it flows southwards via the Disa Stream into the sea at Hout Bay. A large portion of the Disa's catchment is above the mist belt, so moisture precipitated from the "tablecloth" augments the flow during the drought of summer.

### SEEPS – THE SOURCE OF STREAMS

Echo Valley, the source of the Disa Stream, is a giant east-west cleft on Table Mountain's upper plateau. In midwinter it is fed by small cascades tumbling down its cliffs, but for most of the year the only water visible is a glistening film coating the cliffs and dripping from moss beards. Wet, south-facing cliffs like these are the habitat of a unique group of Table Mountain plants and animals.

Perhaps the most typical member of this group is the drip disa *Disa longicornu*. Its large, pale mauve flowers jut out at right angles to the cliff,

while the bulb and roots cling precariously onto a moist layer of moss and smooth sandstone. Other orchids limited to this habitat include *Disa rosea*, *Disa richardiana* and *Disa maculata*, all of which flower in midsummer. They are restricted to high altitudes on the Table Mountain chain, where the cliffs are kept moist in summer by precipitation from the tablecloth.

At the top end of Echo Valley, where the water percolating from the cliffs reaches more level ground, vegetation grows luxuriantly in extensive peat seeps. Here the thick layer of fine organic sediments and sponge-like peat absorbs water in times

*The drip disa* Disa longi-cornu *(1) is one of a group of summer-flowering, high-altitude orchids that depends on moisture precipitated from the table-cloth. Moss-blanketed cliffs at the source of streams on the Back Table (2) and at the aqueduct (3) are typical habitat for such orchids.*

# The sundews

The sundews, all members of the genus *Drosera*, compensate for the paucity of nutrients in seeps by obtaining their nitrogen and phosphorus not from the soil, but from insects that they capture and devour. Their leaves are coated in a dense pile of glandular tentacles, each tipped with a glistening drop of sticky fluid. Contact with only one of these droplets is enough to make the initial capture, but neighbouring tentacles soon respond by bending in towards the prey until they too touch the victim. Movement is achieved through the rapid multiplication and growth of cells on one side of the tentacle only. In time, the leaf itself begins coiling around the insect, by the same process of differential cell growth. Once it is thoroughly ensnared, digestive enzymes in the glue break down the insect and the nutrients released from its body are absorbed directly into the leaf.

As anyone who has tried to induce this behaviour knows, sundews are able to distinguish between edible insects and inedible leaves or stones through complex biochemical pathways, similar to those used for scent detection in our own noses.

1

*Trapped by sticky tentacles, this fly (**1**) will soon be digested by powerful enzymes in the glistening droplets (**2**) that give sundews their name. There are nine species of sundews on the Cape Peninsula, ranging from the large* Drosera capensis *(**3**) to the minute* D. trinervia *(**4**).*

2

3

4

of plenty and releases it throughout the year, constantly supplying the Disa Stream. Typical seep shrubs are the fonteinbos *Berzelia abrotanoides*, with its white bobble-like inflorescences, the bright white marsh daisy *Osmitopsis asteriscoides* and the lanky bloukeur *Psoralea pinnata*, one of the tallest fynbos plants. In between them is a dense bed of restios, including the thick-stalked *Chondropetalum mucronatum*, the elegant *Elegia capensis*, and mattresses of *Anthochortus crinalis*.

Despite their deep layers of peaty soil, seeps are not the nutrient-rich habitats one would expect. Because they are so waterlogged, little oxygen is able to permeate the soil, so natural decomposition and recycling of nutrients is inhibited. The shortage of oxygen also limits root growth, further restricting nutrient uptake by plants. The seep specialists are adapted to survive and thrive under these conditions, which other plants would find intolerable.

Among the seep specialists are some particularly rare Peninsula plants. The most striking is the bokmakieriestert *Witsenia maura*, a peculiar woody member of the iris family with velvety black and

4

5

yellow flowers that resemble the markings of the bokmakierie shrike. Even rarer is *Erica heleogena* (its species name means "born from the marsh") that grows only in Klawervlei on Red Hill. The three conebush species that are endemic to the Peninsula area are also associated with seeps or wet cliffs, and all are included in the Red Data Book because of their threatened status. The Peninsula conebush *Leucadendron strobilinum* has its stronghold on rocky south-facing slopes and wet cliffs on

**4** *A typical seep plant, the bloukeur* Psoralea pinnata *is also one of the tallest fynbos shrubs.*
**5** *Once common in waterlogged areas on the Cape Flats, the conebush* Leucadendron floridum *now survives as only two populations totalling 500 plants.*

Table Mountain, the acacia-leaf conebush *Leucaden-dron macowanii* is restricted to streamside seeps near Smitswinkel Bay, while the flats conebush *Leucadendron floridum*, once common on water-logged soil on the Cape Flats, now survives as only two populations totalling 500 plants.

A characteristic sound of mountain seeps on the Peninsula is the high-pitched, insect-like chirp of the moss frog *Arthroleptella lightfooti*, one of only two vertebrate species endemic to the Cape Peninsula, the other being the Table Mountain ghost frog. It is distinguishable from its nearest rel-atives only by its call, which differs slightly in fre-quency, duration and number of pulses from that of related species. New species of frogs are often described on the basis of their call alone, as female

frogs will only respond to calling males of the same species, a strategy to prevent interbreeding.

Moss frogs are common along the Table Mountain chain, but are difficult to find because they are only about 15 millimetres long and call from concealed positions in the dense under-growth of seeps. The female lays her small batch of eggs inside a mossy nest, and when the tadpoles emerge their hind legs are already fully formed. At first they wriggle around in the moss, but within a day or two the tail has been absorbed, they have developed front legs, and they hop away as minute froglets measuring all of half a centimetre.

Another frog often encountered in seeps, mainly because of its habit of launching itself from the restios when disturbed, is the banded stream frog *Strongylopus bonaespei*. This beautifully patterned frog has such exceptionally long toes that the foot is longer than the head and body! Its tadpoles are commonly seen in shallow water-filled depressions in seeps.

Fire is an integral part of the natural life cycle of a seep. On a recently burned slope, the seeps stand out as patches of green because their vegetation recovers faster than that of the surrounding drier areas. Restio seedlings and cock's comb ferns

*Schizaea pectinata*, uncoiling like green watch springs, are among the first to appear, but the excit-ing discoveries are the bulb plants, the first to flower being the seep-loving fire lily *Cyrtanthus ventri-cosus*. Later, when spring comes, the seeps will become an orchid hunter's paradise, with *Disa race-mosa*, *Disa tenuifolia* and *Disa filicornis* all flowering for the first time after years of dormancy.

## DARK WATERS

Streams in the fynbos region are often referred to as blackwater streams, because their characteristic amber colour is so intense in deep pools that they appear black and bottomless. In smaller volumes the stream water has the golden hue of weak tea, which is no coincidence as in both solutions the colour is derived from chemical compounds in the leaves of plants. Plants produce these chemicals, called polyphenols, to defend themselves from herbivores, and when leached out of leaves they pigment the water. Growing in the nutrient-poor soils of the south-western Cape, plants cannot afford to replace leaves lost to herbivores, which may be the reason why they contain particularly high quantities of polyphenols.

Soils also play a role in determining water colour. When blackwater filters through clay soils, the

**1** *The chirping call of the diminutive moss frog* Arthroleptella lightfooti *is a characteristic sound of the seeps of the upper plateau. It is one of only two verteb-rate species endemic to the Cape Peninsula.*
**2** *Excessively long toes are the driving force behind the spectacular leap of the banded stream frog* Strongylopus bonaespei, *which lives in seeps and restio beds at high altitude.*
**3** *The golden-brown water of the streams on Table Mountain owes its colour to chemical compounds called polyphenols, which are leached from plants by rain-water. Plants are thought to produce polyphenols mainly as a herbivore deterrent.*

polyphenols become chemically attached to the surfaces of the clay granules, and the water loses its colour. This explains why some streams in the south-western Cape are clear and unstained. For example, Platteklip and Silver streams on the north face of Table Mountain are both relatively clear streams because of the granite-derived clay in their catchments. The white "builders' sand" that dominates the catchments of most other streams on the Cape Peninsula has no stain-retaining ability.

The pigment in blackwater streams reduces light penetration, and by doing so limits photosynthesis and hence food production by aquatic plants, with a ripple effect throughout the food chain. The scarcity of water birds on blackwater ponds and streams can be attributed to this low productivity.

Polyphenols not only pigment the stream water, but also make it acidic and mildly toxic. Many stream animals are pH-sensitive, and because those in the fynbos region are adapted to low pH, they are generally unable to spread to other regions. This may partly account for the high endemism of the fynbos stream fauna. The Cape platanna *Xenopus gilli*, for example, occurs mainly in the acidic blackwater lakelets of the Cape Point flats, with a handful of other populations scattered along the coastal plain between Cape Point and Cape Agulhas.

The common platanna *Xenopus laevis* prefers clear water. It is widely distributed in Africa, and thrives in man-made and disturbed waterbodies. Human activity has encouraged its recent spread into areas such as the Cape Peninsula, where formerly only the Cape platanna could survive. Now the two species are hybridising, threatening the survival of the Cape platanna.

### LIFE IN THE FAST LANE

Staying in one place without being swept downstream is a constant challenge for mountain stream animals. Some, such as galaxias fish and whirligig beetles, swim almost constantly to maintain their

4 *Life in the fast lane is rewarding for blackfly larvae, which reap a rich harvest of suspended organic particles from the rushing film of water. Mucus-coated fans on the head filter the particles from the current and are periodically drawn through the mouthparts to be scraped of food and recoated.*

position, and have streamlined contours and smooth surfaces coated in mucus or varnish-like secretions to minimise drag. Others stay in the slower-moving water along the banks or in the thin layer of almost static water close to the streambed, called the boundary layer. For example, some mayfly nymphs have flattened bodies little more than a millimetre thick, enabling them to remain within the thin boundary layer on top of rocks in swiftly flowing areas. Their shield-shaped heads deflect the current so that they are forced against the rock surface, rather than being lifted off and swept away. Table Mountain ghost frogs also use their flattened heads to deflect the current in a strongly flowing stream. Raising their haunches high and keeping their heads low, they power-walk upstream, the force of the water pushing them down against the streambed.

Caddisfly larvae have another solution. They live inside tubular mobile homes, partly constructed

from sand grains or other available material. Apart from providing a refuge from predators, these sturdy homes act as ballast, preventing the larvae from being swept away by the current.

Blackfly larvae are filter-feeders, and have no need to move around as the current brings their food to them. They attach themselves to rocks with an adhesive pad of silken threads, and have a silk safety-line to halt their downward drift in the event that they are swept off their perches.

Stream organisms have found just as many and varied innovative methods of obtaining oxygen. Many stream insects, having evolved from terrestrial ancestors, breathe air. Water scorpions and rat-tailed maggots, for example, have long snorkel-like appendages that they poke out of the water, while waterbeetles surface periodically to capture a bubble of air in an underwing chamber. Most aquatic insects, however, are able to take up dissolved oxygen from the water. The simplest way of obtaining oxygen is directly through the softer, more membranous parts of the body wall, and in many aquatic insects the surface area of these parts is increased to maximise oxygen uptake. Mayflies and dobsonflies have outgrowths of membranous tissue on the abdomen that act as gills, while damselfly nymphs have three plate-like gills on the tip of the abdomen and dragonfly nymphs have gills inside the rectum, which they irrigate by drawing water in and out of the rectal chamber.

## MOUNTAIN STREAM MENUS

As a river progresses from the steep, rocky kloofs to the sandy estuary, it undergoes gradual changes. Not only are there obvious physical changes in the speed of flow, the width and depth of the river, and the riverbed topography, there are also subtle changes in temperature, oxygen availability and water chemistry. Animals and plants are adapted to live in particular conditions along this continuum.

Food is an important determinant of the animal community found at any point along the river. In the headwaters there are few aquatic plants because of the paucity of nutrients and shading by overhanging forest trees. Instead, headwater animals rely on fallen leaves and other plant material from streambank vegetation. Most are adapted for shredding this crude form of food into digestible

*Sedges* Isolepis digitata *flourish in the sunny upper reaches of Disa Stream, but water plants are scarce in most of the shaded streams on Table Mountain, and herbivorous stream animals have to depend on windfall leaves from overhanging trees for their survival.*

# A frog that cannot swim

When the rain pours down and dark clouds hide the mountain from view, the rain frogs emerge from the soil. They have waited underground throughout the dry summer for this moment. The frenzy of feeding and mating that follows will only come to an end when the earth dries out again.

Cape rain frogs *Breviceps gibbosus* are common on the lower slopes of Table Mountain and flourish in suburban gardens, but they are more likely to be heard than seen. Their calls are loud and clear, but finding the frogs is difficult because they may be calling from just below the soil surface or from under a pile of leaf litter.

Higher up the mountain, on steeper, rockier ground, the higher pitch of the frog chorus marks the habitat limit of the mountain rain frog *Breviceps montanus*. These frogs are less than half the size of their low-altitude relatives, and are also much more agile. They often hide under rotten logs or in small pockets of damp leaf material, so they do not need the large areas of soft, loamy soil that are a prerequisite for Cape rain frogs, limiting these amphibians to the shale- or granite-derived soils of the lower slopes.

In both frog species the female locates the male by his whistling call, and she may even be able to select a good partner from a

**1** *A Cape rain frog* Breviceps gibbosus *peers out from a well-used burrow.*
**2** *The mountain rain frog* Breviceps montanus *replaces the Cape rain frog on Table Mountain's upper slopes.*
**3** *His throat inflated with song, a bystander tries to seduce a female rain frog* Breviceps gibbosus *away from her mating partner.*

distance, simply by listening to his song. Calling males attract not only females, but also other males hoping to intercept them. If there is more than one male on the scene by the time the female arrives, the males compete with each other for access to her. The female benefits from this rivalry, because the male who wins the battle is likely to pass his superior qualities on to her offspring. If a male can stay in the lead long enough, he may get a grip on the female's globular body. He then secretes a fluid from his skin glands that glues him firmly to his partner, after which all attempts by the other males to dislodge him from his privileged position are in vain.

Once the female has found a suitable spot, she starts digging with her hind feet, and with a corkscrew motion the pair disappear, rear first, into the soft soil. After she has released her eggs they are fertilised by the male, and the developing tadpoles wriggle around inside their jelly capsules until they have completed their metamorphosis. They emerge as fully developed frogs, which need only enough water to keep the soil moist and their skins wet. In fact, rain frogs cannot swim, and should they land in a deep puddle they simply inflate themselves with air and float around like a beachball until they are blown ashore.

pieces, and some also derive a substantial portion of their nourishment from fungi and bacteria living on the leaf surfaces.

The replacement of natural streambank vegetation with alien plants, such as the pine plantations bordering Cecilia Stream and Newlands Stream, or the invasive species in Diep Kloof and Orange Kloof, has a major impact on stream communities. The leaves of alien plants are not only nutritionally very different from local plants, they are also shed at different times of the year. This may explain why ghost frog tadpoles are rare or absent from Cecilia Ravine, infested by pines and poplars.

Once in the stream, leaves do not get swept away as quickly as one might think. Many get stuck in backwaters and cobbled areas, and not surprisingly, these are also the sites most favoured by leaf-shredding animals. The smooth, concrete surfaces of canalised rivers are barren deserts to most stream animals, being devoid of both suitable habitat and trapped food.

### THE DIVERSITY OF STREAM LIFE

The most conspicuous of the small animals in the streams on Table Mountain are the shrimp-like

amphipods (order Amphipoda), related to the familiar beach hoppers. There are 11 freshwater species on the Cape Peninsula, seven of which are endemic. For example, *Aquadulcaris crassicornis* and *Aquadulcaris marunguis* occur only in streams on Table Mountain, *Aquadulcaris pheronyx* has been found only on Constantiaberg and *Paramelita barnardi* is known only from the subterranean streams in the Kalk Bay caves.

But the species most often encountered on Table Mountain are the pink-tinged *Paramelita capensis*, particularly common in Myburgh's Ravine and Silvermine Stream, and *Paramelita nigroculus*, easily distinguishable by its black eyes and common in the upper reaches of Skeleton and Window gorges. Both feed on leaves and other coarse plant material, reducing them to a skeletal network of veins. As summer approaches and leaf fall increases, their numbers rapidly build up, reaching densities of 12 000 individuals per square metre, only to plummet again as the streams dry up towards the end of summer. In April, pools in Myburgh's Ravine are often carpeted in a layer of *Paramelita capensis* several individuals thick, but a month later the amphipods have died off and have been replaced by masses of scavenging flatworms. Some lucky amphipods presumably survive the summer deep in the rocky bed of the stream and give rise to new colonies at the start of winter. This yearly reduction down to small groups of founder individuals may be the driving force for the evolutionary divergence that has created so many endemic amphipod species on the Peninsula.

Cadddisfly larvae (order Trichoptera) are the hermit crabs of freshwater streams. Each species uses different building materials, such as leaf fragments, bark, sand grains or twigs, held together with silk, to construct its tubular mobile home. Like amphipods, most caddisfly larvae are leaf-shredders, but some are able to harvest suspended particles from the current by spinning funnel-shaped silken nets between twigs and rocks on the streambed. The ability to spin silk is indicative of the close taxonomic relationship between these insects and moths and butterflies.

When the larva is fully grown, it pupates inside its protective case. The adults that emerge resemble small moths with hairy wings held tent-like over the body, but they are poor flyers and prefer to run over streamside boulders. The female caddisfly lays peculiar egg masses that swell into transparent blobs of jelly, sometimes seen dangling from overhanging streamside rocks.

There are 18 species of caddisfly on the Peninsula, and two of these are endemic. Only the adults of

*1 The river crab Potamonautes perlatus is the largest invertebrate in the Cape Peninsula's streams, and is an important decomposer of dead plant and animal matter. By filling its gill chambers with water, the river crab can move considerable distances overland in search of better feeding grounds.*
*2 In a matter of days, a submerged leaf of a forest tree is reduced to a skeleton by a throng of hungry black-eyed amphipods Paramelita nigroculus. By breaking plant material down into small fragments, amphipods and other leaf-shredders make food available to animals downstream.*

*Leptocerus tabularis* have been described, as its larvae have never been seen. Conversely, only the larvae and pupae of *Petroplax caricis* are known, from specimens collected in Platteklip Stream. Its slightly curved larval tube is about a centimetre long and constructed from sand grains, with small pebbles attached at each end.

Mayflies (order Ephemeroptera) are the most celebrated of aquatic insects, for these are the "flies" that give fly-fishing its name. Many of the delicately tied decoys are made to resemble adult and immature mayflies, which are an important food source for freshwater fish. Unlike caddisflies, mayflies do not undergo a complete metamorphosis. There is no pupal stage and no true larva; instead, mayflies have an aquatic nymph, which resembles the adult. Both have three (two in some species) long tail filaments which trail behind them, a single claw on the end of each foot, and compound eyes. However, the nymph differs from the adult in that it lacks wings and has rows of gills along its abdomen.

The nymphs of most mayflies feed by scraping algae and bacteria off rock surfaces, although some, like the south-western Cape's widespread Worcester dark blue *Tricorythus discolor*, filter-feed by using dense bristles on their mouthparts and front legs to trap particles in the current. There are eight species of mayflies in the streams of the Cape Peninsula, none of which is endemic.

Through a series of moults, the mayfly nymph comes to resemble the adult more closely, with the wing buds developing at each moult until they are clearly visible. Eventually the nymph crawls out of the water and moults into the winged form of the adult. As the name of the order implies, the adult phase is ephemeral, and the mayflies live only long enough to find a mate and lay their eggs. They cannot eat during their brief lifetime and their gut is filled with nothing but air, which provides buoyancy for their graceful flight.

Living alongside the mayfly nymphs are the less common stonefly nymphs (order Plecoptera). Superficially the two resemble one another, but closer inspection will reveal that the stonefly nymphs have only two tail filaments, two claws on each foot, conspicuous antennae, and gills that are hidden on the underside of the nymph, if present at all. As adults, stoneflies have wings that lie flat over the abdomen, while those of mayflies stand upright.

Stonefly nymphs are most common on and under rocks that protrude above the water surface, as these are better at trapping leaves than submerged rocks and thus provide more readily available food. Since they can survive only in clear, unpolluted

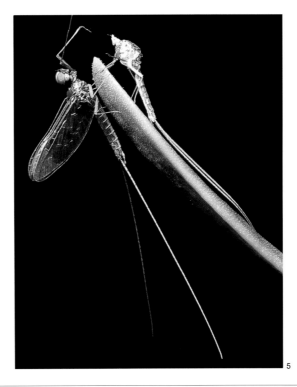

**3** *In summer, Cape amphipods* Paramelita capensis *reach high densities in seasonal streams, but only a handful will survive the dry months of autumn to give rise to new populations when the rivers swell in winter.*
**4** *Depending on the species, caddisfly larvae construct tubular mobile homes from sand grains, small pebbles, or fragments of leaves and bark.*
**5** *An adult mayfly rests alongside its recently shed exoskeleton, the second in a unique two-stage moult.*

mountain streams, they are effectively used as an indicator of water quality.

Apart from some caddisflies and mayflies, the only other filter-feeding stream insects belong to the order of true flies, the Diptera. By far the most common are the club-shaped larvae of blackflies (family Simuliidae), usually found in small colonies on top of smooth boulders in areas of uniform flow. The swollen tail end of their abdomen is attached to the rock, while the head trails downstream. Protruding from the head are two mucus-covered

fans that trap tiny organic particles as they hurtle past in the current. The fans are periodically drawn through the mouthparts, cleaned of old mucus and trapped particles, and recoated before being thrust out into the current again.

Like all true flies, blackflies undergo a complete metamorphosis from a legless larva into a winged adult. The larvae spin a slipper-shaped cocoon, which is attached to the rock surface and open at one end so that the branched gills can protrude into the current. When the adult is ready to emerge, the pupal skin splits and a bubble of air shoots the insect to the surface, where it immediately unfurls its wings and flies off.

While the blackflies filter, the mayflies scrape and the amphipods shred, the predators watch as they lie in ambush. The nymph of the dragonfly (order Odonata) has large compound eyes, giving it excellent all-round vision. It looks a harmless creature, but its secret weapon is its modified lower lip that can be rapidly extended to strike out at prey. If disturbed, the nymph shoots away, propelling itself with a powerful jet of water squirted from the muscular rectum.

Adult dragonflies are expert aerial hunters. Their bristled legs form a basket below their jaws with which small flying insects are plucked from the air. Regular patrol flights are undertaken in search of mates and prey, after which they return to a favourite perch at the water's edge.

A feature unique to members of the order Odonata is the curious method of mating, during which the male clasps the female firmly behind her head with pincers on the end of his abdomen.

*1 Tied in a love knot, a male dragonfly grips the duller female behind her head with pincers on the tip of his abdomen. She in turn bends her body forward to make contact with his sperm-transferring device, which also scoops out the sperm of other males that have already mated with her.*
*2 The dragonfly nymph is a fearsome predator that hunts among the leaves at the bottom of a pool.*

3

the stems of plants just above or below the water surface, using sharp blades situated on the end of her abdomen.

Alderfly larvae (order Megaloptera) also hunt in fast, cold mountain streams. They are among the largest insects in the streams on Table Mountain, reaching lengths of about 4 centimetres, and are easily identifiable by the eight pairs of prong-like gills on each of the abdominal segments. They used to be taxonomically grouped with the lacewings and antlions, and indeed, the larvae of all three

The female bends her abdomen forward until the tip comes into contact with the bizarre sperm-transferring device on the second segment of the male's abdomen. This barbed organ not only transfers sperm to the female, but also scoops out the sperm of any other males with which the female might already have mated. In many species the male takes off once he has the female firmly held, and they fly off in tandem to mate on the wing. Then the pair swoops low over the water surface so that the female can lay her eggs, repeatedly dipping the tip of her abdomen into the water. The attached male may assist to some extent in pulling her free from the water's surface.

Damselflies are the slender cousins of dragonflies, the two being the only members of the order Odonata. The nymphs of damselflies closely resemble those of dragonflies, and they also hunt small aquatic creatures with an extensible lower lip. However, they lack the dragonfly's novel rectal device and rely instead on a three-finned tail to propel themselves. Damselfly nymphs are common in Table Mountain's swift mountain streams, where they cling to the vertical walls of submerged boulders, while their cousins prefer quieter pools with muddy bottoms.

The adults of the two sub-orders are also very similar, but can easily be distinguished by the position of the wings at rest. The stiff wings of dragonflies project at right angles to the body, while those of damselflies lie parallel to the abdomen. Damselflies share the unique mating behaviour of dragonflies, but differ in the egg-laying technique. The female lays her eggs in slits that she cuts into

*3 The more agile cousins of dragonflies, damselfly nymphs prefer to hunt on submerged boulders.*
*4 Unlike dragonflies, damselflies hold their wings parallel to their slender bodies when at rest. These two members of the order Odonata, together with the mayflies of the order Ephemeroptera, are the only insects that cannot flex their wings, regarded as a primitive feature.*

4

have powerful sickle-shaped mandibles that have earned alderfly larvae the name "toe biters". The adults also resemble one another in having large wings that they keep folded over their abdomen when at rest. The order Megaloptera is an ancient one with an almost worldwide distribution, but on the African continent it seems to be entirely confined to South Africa.

Only one fish species is likely to be encountered in the streams on Table Mountain, and that is the Cape galaxias *Galaxias zebratus*, which is restricted to streams along the Cape coast between the Olifants and Keurbooms rivers. Seldom more than 7 centimetres long, it is scale-less and translucent, although faint barring can be discerned in the adults. This little fish is the only African member of the family Galaxiidae, which like many other Table Mountain plants and animals is well represented

in the southern regions of Australia and South America, implying that it evolved before the break-up of Gondwanaland.

Probably the most effective predators in the streams on Table Mountain are the Cape river frogs *Afrana fuscigula*. These are the commonly encountered frogs that leap unexpectedly from the bank when disturbed and plop into the deepest part of a pool, where they are soon lost behind a smoke screen of stirred-up mud. They have webbed toes and thick and powerful thighs, enabling them to spring from the water's edge to pluck insect morsels from the streamside vegetation.

The males usually call from a partly submerged position in small caves along the edge of big pools. On Table Mountain the call is usually limited to an occasional *chuck*, not nearly as impressive as the chorus of Cape rain frogs or even clicking stream frogs, which have short and frenzied bursts of breeding activity. In Cape river frogs mating and egg-laying occur from October to mid-December on Table Mountain, a few months behind the populations on the Cape Flats. The delayed breeding in the mountain-living frogs may be an adaptation to ensure that the eggs are not washed away when the streams are in full spate in winter.

In deep pools, the tadpoles may grow to enormous sizes and only metamorphose into frogs after a few years. Recently metamorphosed and sub-adult frogs on Table Mountain are usually mustard-coloured with a pale vertebral line.

On the Peninsula, Cape river frogs and their tadpoles are the primary prey of the common brown

1

**1** *The adult alderfly* Taeniochauliodes ochraceopennis *looks very different from its grub-like aquatic larva, known as a toe biter. The larvae are predators of aquatic insects and crustaceans.*
**2** *Cape galaxias* Galaxias zebratus *cluster together in small shoals in shaded pools, where they prey mainly on small floating insects.*

2

# A creature of darkness

Few people have been fortunate enough to see a Table Mountain ghost frog *Heleophryne rosei*. Apart from being very rare, they are also extremely secretive, hiding during the day in deep rock cracks and in caves, and emerging at night to feed on insects (in fact, *Heleophryne* means "the one which is afraid of the sun"). Suction pads on their toes, and minute skin projections that grip like Velcro, enable them to climb the vertical rock faces and waterfalls of the dark, forested gorges on the mountain's eastern slopes, while their flattened bodies can fit into the narrowest of cracks.

The tadpoles are as specialised as the adults. Their mouths are modified into huge suckers, which are so effective for clinging to the underside of submerged rocks that even a midwinter torrent is unlikely to pry them loose. Inside are more than 20 rows of teeth, used for scraping algae, fungi and bacteria from the submerged rocks, but such food is relatively scarce in the tadpoles' shaded, nutrient-poor pools, so they usually take more than a year to mature. This implies that they can only survive in perennial streams, and indeed, their distribution is limited to an area no larger than 8 square kilometres on the east- and south-facing slopes of Table Mountain, encompassing all the perennial mountain streams on the Cape Peninsula. Little is known about the breeding biology of the Table Mountain ghost frog, but at the

onset of the breeding season in early November the mature frogs congregate in deep pools. They spend long periods underwater, and to enhance oxygen uptake through their skin they constantly circulate the water around them by fanning it with their hind feet.

*Heleophryne rosei* is a true child of Table Mountain, the product of millions of years of evolution in isolation. Its closest relative, the Cape ghost frog *Heleophryne purcelli*, lives in the mountain ranges to the east of Table Mountain. Ghost frogs could never survive the long journey across the sun-baked and sandy Cape Flats, so they must have colonised Table Mountain at a time when the Cape was very different from the way it is today. Since then, trapped on their island of rock, the ghost frogs have become specifically adapted to the conditions on Table Mountain, and now look quite different from their relatives across the plain.

**1** *The rare Table Mountain ghost frog* Heleophryne rosei *lives only in the swift-flowing sections of seven streams on Table Mountain, and nowhere else in the world. Adhesive pads on its fingers allow it to climb slippery rock faces, while the tadpole (**2**) has a special sucker mouth for clinging to boulders in torrential streams.*

water snake *Lycodonomorphus rufulus*, although it also takes other frog species and occasionally galaxias. It can be identified by its pinkish belly and orange tongue, which ends in a forked black tip. It is mainly nocturnal but sometimes also hunts during the day, creeping up on prey until it is within striking range, or giving chase if detected. As soon as the teeth latch on, the body is rapidly coiled around the prey to suffocate it, because these snakes have no venom. The prey is swallowed head first, and the jaw can be unhinged to allow the passage of big prey. Several other snakes on the Peninsula, including Cape cobras and boomslang, also prey on frogs as part of their diet.

The Cape clawless otter *Aonyx capensis* and the water mongoose *Atilax paludinosus* are top predators in the aquatic ecosystem. On the Cape Peninsula most otters live along the coast and are equally at home feeding in freshwater systems or the sea. They spend the day in holts that are typically in dry, sandy places under overhanging rocks or in dense coastal vegetation, and which have a characteristic strong musky odour. Intensive coastal development has severed the vital link between terrestrial and marine habitats along most of the Peninsula, so otters are rarely seen. The scats of otters usually contain the crushed exoskeletons of crabs and crayfish, although frogs and fish are also taken. In contrast, the feeding places of water mongooses, often found on flat rocks along the streambank, are identifiable by piles of intact crab carapaces and pincers, as these are too hard for a mongoose to crack.

**HEADING FOR THE SEA**

On the lower slopes, mountain streams join together and continue their journey towards the sea as mature rivers. The middle and lower reaches of rivers usually have their own wealth of flora and fauna, but on the Cape Peninsula all the larger rivers flow through densely urbanised areas, where

*1* Cape river frogs Afrana fuscigula *are the most commonly encountered frogs on Table Mountain, as they often sit in conspicuous positions on stream banks and boulders. Their impressive leaping abilities allow them to catch dragonflies and other insect prey in midair.*

*2* A specialist aquatic hunter, a juvenile brown water snake Lycodonomorphus rufulus *makes a meal of a tadpole in Window Stream. Water snakes have no toxin and kill by constriction.*

they are channelled into bleak concrete canals and fed with effluent from the city. Needless to say, very little life can survive in this unnatural environment.

The lower reaches of the Disa River in Hout Bay are not canalised, but are almost as degraded. The loss of natural bank vegetation and its replacement by shallow-rooted invasive alien plants has resulted in severe erosion of the banks and instability of the riverbed. The problem is aggravated by the loss of peripheral wetlands in the lower valley. These wetlands were once dominated by dense growths of the palmiet *Prionium serratum*, which buffered the force of winter spates. One bizarre consequence of the rapid runoff now is that the rare leopard toads *Bufo pantherinus*, which do not inhabit water as adults but return to the lower reaches of the Disa River to breed, are occasionally swept out to sea during rainstorms.

In the final stage of their development, rivers draining the eastern slopes of Table Mountain meander across the Cape Flats on their way to either False Bay or Table Bay. Here the riverbed consists of smooth, fine sediment made up of particles that were eroded out of the catchment by swiftly flowing waters and then deposited in these slow, lower reaches. Some animals thrive in these nutrient-rich environments, particularly introduced lumbriculid worms, the aquatic relatives of earthworms, which process the sediments to extract organic matter. These worms contain haemoglobin in their blood so that they can absorb what little oxygen exists in the warm, polluted waters.

Estuaries, at the interface between river and sea, are particularly challenging environments for aquatic animals and plants. Tides and rainfall cause daily and seasonal fluxes in salinity, conditions that only estuarine specialists can survive. Unfortunately, most of the Cape Flats' estuaries have been severely impacted by canalisation, development or siltation. Human activities in the catchment accelerate siltation, often resulting in closure of estuary mouths, particularly during summer low-flow periods. This in turn affects local fisheries, because many sea fishes use the quiet waters of estuaries as breeding grounds and nursery areas.

Coastal lakes in the shadow of Table Mountain, such as Rietvlei, Rondevlei and Zeekoevlei, are

3

4

**3** *On the first three warm days in August, leopard toads* Bufo pantherinus *congregate at large waterbodies on the Peninsula lowlands to breed, but increasing urbanisation is causing a steady decline in yearly attendance.*
**4** *On the Cape Peninsula the primarily nocturnal Cape clawless otter* Aonyx capensis *hunts in both freshwater and marine habitats for frogs, crabs and fish, and spends the day in secluded holts on land.*

plagued by excessive growth of weeds and algae, because unlike estuaries they are not regularly flushed. Pollution from the catchment, including runoff from fertilised fields and gardens, provides the plants with an unlimited supply of nutrients, allowing them to thrive. The dense growth not only interferes with water sports, but also reduces light penetration into the water, leading to additional ecological changes. Furthermore, many blue-green algae, such as *Macrocystis aeruginosa*, have toxic phases that pose a health risk. As the weeds and algae die, their decomposition promotes bacterial activity and causes further siltation. The resulting shallowing of the lake allows the encroachment of lake-edge plants, such as the bulrush *Typha capensis*, the grass *Paspalum vaginatum* and the reed *Phragmites australis*.

## TEMPORARY WETLANDS OF THE FLATS

During the winter rainy season, low-lying areas on the Cape Flats fill with water and become temporary wetlands. On Kenilworth Racecourse these wetlands are the stronghold of the microfrog *Microbatrachella capensis*, the most endangered frog species in Africa, with the only other populations occurring in the Kleinmond area. When fully grown at about 15 millimetres long, microfrogs are various shades of brown with a marbled pattern on the underside, while younger individuals are also brown but are covered in small green spots, or have pale green streaks on their flanks. The adults are often mistaken for the common caco *Cacosternum boettgeri*, which is abundant in these habitats. Unlike the microfrog, however, the caco has a flattened body and toes that are not webbed.

1

3

*1 The microfrog Microbatrachella capensis is the most endangered frog in South Africa. It breeds in temporary vleis in lowland fynbos on the Cape Flats, where today only one or two small populations still survive.*

*2 Arum lily frogs Hyperolius horstocki are quite widely distributed in the south-western and southern Cape, but they too are threatened by the loss of their lowland habitat through urbanisation.*

*3 No temporary wetland on the Cape Flats is complete without a breeding population of orange-throated longclaws Macronyx capensis.*

2

The calls of the two species are quite distinct, the caco's consisting of about eight high-pitched, explosive clicks per second, while that of the microfrog is a single, clear chirping note. Microfrogs breed in winter, when the vleis are at their fullest. The males typically call from partly submerged restio clumps, which provide protection as well as abundant food, because insects take refuge here from the rising water levels. Microfrogs in turn sometimes make a meal for marsh terrapins *Pelomedusa subrufa*, which are common in the Kenilworth Racecourse wetlands.

The most characteristic bird of temporary wetlands is the orangethroated longclaw *Macronyx capensis*. It is often seen on Milnerton Racecourse and Rondebosch Common because of its unmistakable habit of displaying its bright throat from the top of bushes. A much rarer bird of marshy habitats is the marsh owl *Asio capensis*. Only small populations exist in the south-western Cape, but a pair has been seen at Kenilworth Racecourse.

## QUENCHING THE CITY'S THIRST

It was the availability of fresh water, and its proximity to good anchorage, that motivated the Dutch East India Company to establish a settlement in the shadow of Table Mountain in 1652. However, the city centre is located on the drier northern side of the mountain, while most of the water that falls on the mountain drains southwards into Hout Bay. In 1891, in order to re-route this bountiful supply of water, the Woodhead Tunnel was built through the Apostles, connecting the Disa River to Slangolie Ravine on the west face. The water was then piped around the mountain to the Molteno Reservoir, hence the "pipe track" now enjoyed by scores of walkers every day. The instability of Slangolie Ravine resulted in the Woodhead Tunnel later being replaced by the Apostle Tunnel, which exits on Woodhead Buttress and is still in use today.

The Woodhead and the Hely-Hutchinson reservoirs were built across the Disa River on the Back Table to improve the year-round water supply to the tunnel. In addition, three more dams – the Victoria, Alexandra and De Villiers – were built across the original Disa Stream to feed a filtration plant near Constantia Nek, from where the water is distributed to the suburbs.

Stone aqueducts were also built on top of the mountain to extend the size of the Disa's catchment and improve the supply to the dams. The largest of these diverts water from the catchment of Window Stream, and is partly to blame for the stream's upper reaches being dry in summer, which greatly decreases the number of suitable habitats for Table Mountain's endemic stream animals. Further downstream, more water is piped away to an off-stream dam and used for irrigation at the National Botanical Garden at Kirstenbosch. A second, smaller aqueduct on top of the mountain transfers water from Vaalkat Stream into De Villiers Dam.

These days the Window Aqueduct is a good place to see red disas, but this does not nearly compensate for the huge areas of pristine stream and seep habitat that were inundated by the dams. Of greater concern is the more than three billion litres of water abstracted from the Disa catchment each year. The Disa gorge, downstream from the dams, is the largest area of suitable habitat for the Table Mountain ghost frog *Heleophryne rosei*, and there is no question that the water abstraction has serious consequences for this and many other species. Dams also impact downstream aquatic habitats by radically altering seasonal flow patterns. For example, the lower reaches of the Disa River are buffered from midwinter spates because of the dams, which might make it possible for the Cape river frog *Afrana fuscigula* to invade habitats normally occupied only by ghost frogs and their torrent-adapted tadpoles.

As Cape Town's water demands increase, the construction of more dams in the Cape mountains seems inevitable. Yet the need for water has recently had one spin-off that is beneficial both to people and the natural environment. The *Working for Water* campaign is a government initiative that employs unskilled people to clear mountain catchments of water-thirsty invasive alien plants. Armed with pangas and herbicides, the labourers are reaping the benefits of job creation, and at the same time safeguarding water supplies and returning fynbos slopes to their former glory.

**4** *Great wheels control the outflow of water from the Hely-Hutchinson Dam on the Back Table. By depriving or flooding the downstream reaches of the Disa River, humans determine the fate of ghost frog tadpoles and a wealth of other endemic stream creatures. Currently 3.3 billion litres are extracted from the Disa River each year, and an additional 740 million litres from the Original Disa Stream.*

# Afterword

*1 Urbanisation of the southern Peninsula has infringed on the foraging grounds of chacma baboons Papio ursinus, with the result that they regularly enter houses and raid dustbins in search of food.*

*2 Green shading indicates the 30 000 hectare conservation area known as the Cape Peninsula Protected Natural Environment. Public land comprises 80 per cent of this area and forms the core of the newly proclaimed Cape Peninsula National Park. Negotiations are in progress to include the remaining privately owned land into the park.*

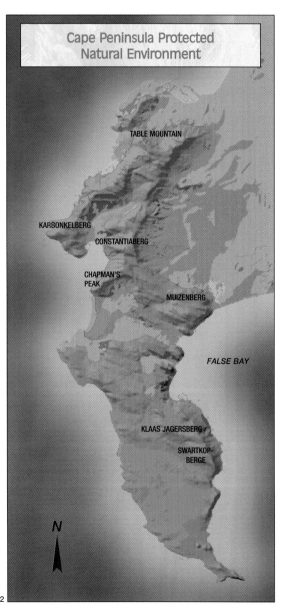

Cape Peninsula Protected Natural Environment

TABLE MOUNTAIN

KARBONKELBERG

CONSTANTIABERG

CHAPMAN'S PEAK

MUIZENBERG

FALSE BAY

KLAAS JAGERSBERG

SWARTKOP-BERGE

N

2

t is impossible to do justice to the biological wealth of the Cape Peninsula in one book. At most, we hope that we have encouraged the growing interest in the animals and plants of the area, and in so doing, stimulated the desire to conserve this life in all its strange and beautiful forms. In particular, we aimed to cultivate an appreciation for the smaller creatures and plants – the secret life that is often overlooked, but which needs our conservation efforts just as urgently as the big mammals of Africa.

Although he saw only the specimens brought to Europe by eighteenth-century collectors, Linnaeus observed that "There is no place in the world with so many rare plants, animals, insects, and other wonders of Nature as Africa, and it seems as if they have been concentrated [in] the Cape". As the biological exploration of the planet proceeded, it soon became evident that the Cape, and especially the Cape Peninsula, was a global centre for special and endemic plants and animals. Current figures compiled from the vast store of information contained in herbariums and museum collections indicate that about 100 animals and 160 plants are restricted to the Cape Peninsula. These jewels in the crown are what make this mountainous promontory unique in Africa and the world.

Although biologists from foreign countries find it hard to believe, several of the Peninsula's endemic species exist as single populations sometimes numbering less than a hundred individuals. An understanding of their natural history, demography and distribution is clearly essential if they are to be conserved, and regular population censuses are required. Much work remains to be done, as proved by the recent discovery of an endemic disa on Devil's Peak, little more than a stone's throw from the city centre.

Just as species can be rare or endangered, habitats and unique communities of species can also be threatened. Rare and threatened habitats on the Cape Peninsula include perennial streams, renosterveld and sand plain fynbos, the latter surviving as a scattering of small, poorly conserved fragments. In this decade alone, the increasing urbanisation of lowlands has resulted in the extinction of the last wild populations of *Erica bolusiae* and *Erica turgida*, although both species survive in cultivation at Kirstenbosch.

Throughout this book we have stressed the interactions between plants and animals, and their relationship to the soil, geology, topography, weather and fire. The conservation of species hinges on the conservation of the processes that govern their lives. Fire is an example of one such ecological process that is clearly very important in fynbos landscapes, and the maintenance of fynbos diversity on the Cape Peninsula depends to a large extent on good fire management. However, controlled burns on the Peninsula are often opposed because of smoke pollution and a perceived threat to property; a wider understanding of the vital role of fire could make the conservation manager's job a lot easier.

Less obvious ecological processes, such as pollination and seed dispersal, are also vital for fynbos conservation, but some are easily disrupted. For example, in areas invaded by Argentine ants, the native ants normally responsible for seed dispersal of many fynbos plant species have been displaced, and few seedlings of ant-dispersed species can be found. Despite the potentially devastating consequences for the vegetation of the area, the extent of Argentine ant invasion on the Cape Peninsula is not known.

Equally insidious is the loss of obscure pollinating insects, such as long-tongued flies and oil-collecting bees. About 30 plant species on the Cape Peninsula depend on the highly specialised oil-collecting bee for their pollination, so it is disconcerting that recent evidence indicates that the bee is very rare on the Peninsula, perhaps

as a result of the increasing urbanisation of the surrounding lowlands.

A far more obvious threat to biodiversity on the Cape Peninsula is the devastation caused by invasive alien plants, mainly species of Australian *Acacia*. In South Africa, these aliens flourish in the absence of the specialised insects, fungi and other diseases that keep them in check in their home country. Some of these enemies, notably a fungus that attacks the Port Jackson willow *Acacia saligna* and a small wasp that galls the long-leafed wattle *Acacia longifolia*, have now been deliberately introduced from Australia as biological control agents, with spectacular results. Equally encouraging is the progress made by the alien removal programme, in which unskilled labour is trained and employed to clear the Cape Peninsula's natural areas of invasive alien plants. SA National Parks has set the objective of removing all seed-bearing woody invasive plants from the

**3** *Fire can be a blessing in disguise for the fynbos communities of the Cape Peninsula, giving rise to new life, such as these March lilies* Amaryllis belladonna *which appeared soon after a fire on Lion's Head.*

3

Cape Peninsula by the end of 2003. The campaign funded mainly by the Global Environmental Facility has created some 800 employment opportunities for previously unemployed people.

Second only to the problem of alien plant invasion is the threat posed by urban expansion. On the lowlands, much of the damage has already been done, but the future of a significant proportion of privately owned mountain land is still in the balance. Fortunately, some private landowners strive to keep the land under their control in a wild state, but in the case of Oudekraal and Dassenberg, this is clearly not the intention.

The antidote to many of these pressing problems is the good news that a large portion of the natural areas of the Cape Peninsula is in the process of receiving the highest possible protection under South African law. The recent proclamation of the Cape Peninsula National Park will protect an area eventually encompassing 30 000 hectares and stretching from Signal Hill to Cape Point. Previously, this area was under the control of no less than 14 public bodies and 174 private landowners, a conservation manager's nightmare. The long-awaited instatement of a single management authority was a major breakthrough for conservation.

**1** *The trip to the top of Table Mountain by cable car is one of the Cape's most popular tourist attractions, but visitor numbers and behaviour must be managed to ensure that the natural areas of the Peninsula are not degraded.*
**2** *Biodiversity is currently the conservation buzzword, but natural landscapes are just as valuable and equally in need of protection.*

Soon after its proclamation, the new park was given a push-start by a grant of $11.3 million from the Global Environmental Facility, set up by the World Bank and the United Nations to fund conservation projects of global importance in developing countries. Of this amount, $6.3 million will fund the park's start-up costs over the next five years, and $5 million will go to the WWF-administered Table Mountain Fund, which has already raised R10 million from local corporations and private individuals.

In the future, we can look forward to the possibility that the Cape Peninsula National Park will be proclaimed a World Heritage Site, which would be well-deserved recognition of its global importance. World Heritage status would not only ensure protection of the Cape Peninsula under international law, but might also mean easier access to international conservation funding.

However, the question of how the new park will be funded in the long term remains. Despite the massive contribution that the Peninsula makes in attracting tourists and investors to Cape Town, conservation funding is being cut as the government attempts to redress the imbalances of the apartheid era and meet the needs of the burgeoning population. Clearly, the park will have to be self-supporting. Now the challenge is to find innovative ways of generating funds for conservation without negatively impacting the plants, animals and wild landscapes at issue. Currently, tourist facilities are strategically concentrated around the cable car station, at Kirstenbosch and at Cape Point, and there are still many parts of the Peninsula where one can walk for half a day and meet only a handful of fellow hikers. The natural inaccessibility of these areas regulates both the number and quality of visitors, many of whom are attracted by the wilderness ambience of these places. The Cape Peninsula National Park team is faced with the difficult task of managing the increasing numbers of visitors without destroying this ambience.

In a long-term view, education determines the future of conservation areas. With a mountain on their doorstep, educators have a unique opportunity to teach in an outdoor classroom with almost unlimited resources. The Kirstenbosch Botanical Garden, in particular, enriches the lives of hundreds of schoolchildren every week through hands-on experiences with nature. It is only through cultivating the desire to conserve nature out of a sheer appreciation of its wonders that the future of wild areas can ultimately be assured.

**3** *The natural areas of the Cape Peninsula provide a refuge from the hustle and bustle of city life and are an important recreational resource.*

3

**4** *At Camps Bay, as in many other parts of the Peninsula, development is steadily encroaching on the mountain and the sea, severing the ecological link between marine and terrestrial environments and threatening their unique plant and animal life. Today, Table Mountain is an ark afloat in a sea of urbanisation.*

4

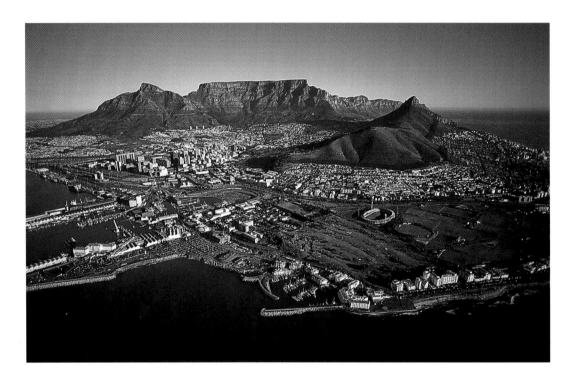

"May you be fully aware of your fortunate lot ... to enjoy ... that
Paradise on Earth, the Cape of Good Hope, which the beneficent
Creator has enriched with his choicest wonders."

CAROLUS LINNAEUS

*Linnaeus (1707–1778) was the Swedish botanist and taxonomist who
developed the system of species classification and nomenclature still used today.
He was the first to describe many species of the Cape Flora.*

# Bibliography

Adamson, R.S. & Salter, T.M. 1950. *Flora of the Cape Peninsula*. Juta, Cape Town.

Bolus, H. 1918. *The orchids of the Cape Peninsula* (2nd edition). Darter Bros, Cape Town.

Bond, P. & Goldblatt, P. 1984. Plants of the Cape flora: a descriptive catalogue. *Journal of South African Botany* 13: 1–455.

Bond, W.J. & van Wilgen, B.W. 1996. *Fire and plants: population and community biology series 14*. Chapman & Hall, London.

Branch, G. & Branch, M. 1981. *The living shores of southern Africa*. C. Struik Publishers, Cape Town.

Branch, G.M., Griffiths, C.L., Branch, M.L. & Beckley, L.E. 1994. *Two Oceans: a guide to the marine life of southern Africa*. David Philip, Cape Town.

Branch, W.R. (Ed.) 1988. South African Red Data Book: reptiles and amphibians. *South African National Scientific Programmes Report No. 151*.

Branch, W.R. 1998. *Field guide to the snakes and other reptiles of southern Africa*. Struik, Cape Town.

Brossy, S. 1989. *A walking guide for the Hout Bay to Simon's Town mountains*. S. Brossy, Cape Town.

Brossy, S. 1991. *A walking guide for Table Mountain* (4th edition). S. Brossy, Cape Town.

Burchell, W. 1822. *Travels in the interior of South Africa, Vols I–II*. Longman, London.

Burman, J. 1991. *The Table Mountain book*. Human & Rousseau, Cape Town.

Cape Peninsula National Park 1998. Draft development framework: channelling visitors in the Cape Peninsula National Park.

Claassen, A.J.M. & Dickson, C.G.C. 1980. *Butterflies of the Table Mountain range*. Struik, Cape Town.

Clark, G.C. & Dickson, C.G.C. 1971. *Life histories of the South African Lycaenid butterflies*. Purnell, Cape Town.

Coates Palgrave, K. 1977. *Trees of southern Africa*. Struik, Cape Town.

Cowling, R.M. (Ed.) 1992. *The ecology of fynbos: nutrients, fire and diversity*. Oxford University Press, Cape Town.

Cowling, R.M. & Richardson, D. 1995. *Fynbos: South Africa's unique floral kingdom*. Fernwood Press, Cape Town.

Cowling, R.M., Richardson, D.M. & Pierce, S.M. (Eds) 1997. *Vegetation of southern Africa*. Cambridge University Press, Cape Town.

CSIR 1993. *Approved paths on Table Mountain*. The Mountain Club of South Africa, Cape Town.

Davies, B.R. & Day, J.A. 1998. *Vanishing waters*. University of Cape Town Press, Cape Town.

De Graaf, G. 1981. *The rodents of southern Africa: notes on their identification, distribution, ecology and taxonomy*. Butterworths, Pretoria.

De Villiers Brownlie & Associates (Eds) 1998. *Cape Peninsula National Park draft development framework comments report: synthesis of written submissions*.

Dickinson, C.G.C. & Kroon, D.M. 1978. *Pennington's butterflies of South Africa*. Donker, Johannesburg.

Filmer, M.R. 1991. *Southern African spiders: an identification guide*. Struik, Cape Town.

Fraser, M. & McMahon, L. 1988. *A fynbos year*. David Philip, Cape Town.

Fraser, M. & McMahon, L. 1994. *Between two shores: flora and fauna of the Cape of Good Hope*. David Philip, Cape Town.

Goldblatt, P. 1986. *The Moraeas of southern Africa: a systematic monograph of the genus in South Africa, Lesotho, Swaziland, Transkei, Botswana, Namibia and Zimbabwe*. National Botanic Gardens, Cape Town.

Goldblatt, P. 1998. *The genus Watsonia: a systematic monograph*. National Botanic Gardens, Cape Town.

Goldblatt, P. & Manning, J. 1998. *Gladiolus in southern Africa*. Fernwood Press, Cape Town.

Gunn, M. & Codd, L.E. 1981. *Botanical exploration of southern Africa*. A.A. Balkema, Cape Town.

Harrison, J.A., Allan, D.G., Underhill, L.G., Herremans, M., Tree, A.J., Parker, V. & Brown, C.J. (Eds) 1997. *The atlas of southern African birds (Vols I–II)*. BirdLife South Africa, Johannesburg.

Hey, D. 1994. *The mountain: an authoritative guide to the Table Mountain chain*. Tafelberg Publishers, Cape Town.

Henning, S.F. & Henning, G.A. 1989. South African Red Data Book: butterflies. *South African National Scientific Programmes Report No. 158*.

Jackson, W.P.U. 1977. *Wildflowers of Table Mountain*. Howard Timmins, Cape Town.

Jackson, W.P.U. 1980. *Wildflowers of the fairest Cape*. Howard Timmins, Cape Town.

Jackson, W.P.U. 1990. *Origins and meanings of names of the South African plant genera*. University of Cape Town, Cape Town.

Kench, J. 1988. *Know Table Mountain*. Chameleon Press, Cape Town.

Kingdon, J. 1990. *Island Africa: the evolution of Africa's rare animals and plants*. Collins, London.

Kingdon, J. 1997. *The Kingdon field guide to African mammals*. Academic Press, London.

Lawrence, R.F. 1953. *The biology of the cryptic fauna of forests with special reference to the indigenous forests of South Africa*. A.A. Balkema, Cape Town.

Lawrence, R.F. 1984. *The centipedes and millipedes of southern Africa: a guide*. A.A. Balkema, Cape Town.

Levin, H., Branch, M., Rappoport, S. & Mitchell, D. 1985. *A field guide to the mushrooms of South Africa*. Struik, Cape Town.

Levyns, M.R. 1929. *Guide to the flora of the Cape Peninsula*. Juta & Co., Cape Town.

Low, B. & Rebelo, A.G. 1996. *Vegetation of South Africa, Lesotho and Swaziland: a companion to the vegetation map of South Africa, Lesotho and Swaziland*. Department of Environmental Affairs and Tourism, Pretoria.

Luckhoff, C.A. 1951. *Table Mountain – history, flora, mountaineering, conservation – our national heritage after three hundred years*. A.A. Balkema, Cape Town.

Mabbutt, J.A. (Ed.) 1952. *The Cape Peninsula*. Maskew Miller, Cape Town.

Maclean, G.L. 1993. *Roberts birds of southern Africa* (6th edition). John Voelcker Bird Book Fund, Cape Town.

Marloth, R. 1913–1932. *The flora of South Africa: with synoptical tables of the genera of higher plants Vols I–VI*. Darter Bros. & Co., Cape Town.

Maytham Kidd, M. 1983. *Cape Peninsula: South African wildflower guide 3*. Botanical Society of South Africa, Claremont.

Moll, E.J. & Scott, L. 1981. *Trees and shrubs of the Cape Peninsula*. Eco-lab Trust Fund, Botany Department, University of Cape Town.

Moll, G. 1987. *Table Mountain: a natural wonder*. The Wildlife Society of Southern Africa, Kirstenhof.

Murray, M. 1964. *Under Lion's Head*. Balkema, Cape Town.

Newman, K. 1992. *Newman's birds of southern Africa* (4th edition). Southern Book Publishers, Halfway House.

Passmore, N.I. & Carruthers, V.C. 1995. *South African frogs: a complete guide*. Southern Book Publishers & Witwatersrand University Press, Johannesburg.

Paterson-Jones, C. 1991. *Table Mountain walks*. Struik Publishers, Cape Town.

Prins, A.J. & Leroux, V. 1986. *South African spiders and scorpions: identification, first aid, and medical treatment*. Anubis Press, Cape Town.

Raven-Hart, R. 1967. *Before Van Riebeeck: callers at South Africa from 1488 to 1652*. Struik, Cape Town.

Rebello, A.C. 1995. *Proteas: a field guide to the proteas of southern Africa*. Fernwood Press, Cape Town.

Rose, W. 1950. *The reptiles and amphibians of southern Africa*. Maskew Miller, Cape Town.

Rourke, J.P. 1980. *The proteas of southern Africa*. Purnell, Cape Town.

Scholtz, C.H. & Holm, E. 1986. *Insects of southern Africa*. Butterworths, Durban.

Schuman, D. & Kirsten, G. 1992. *Ericas of South Africa*. Fernwood Press, Cape Town.

Sinclair, I., Hockey, P. & Tarboton, W. 1993. *Sasol birds of southern Africa*. Struik, Cape Town.

Skaife, S.H. 1938. *South African nature notes: essays of a South African naturalist*. Maskew Miller, Cape Town.

Skaife, S.H. 1979. *African insect life*. Struik, Cape Town.

Skead, C.J. 1980. *Historical mammal incidence in the Cape Province: The western and northern Cape (Vol. I)*. Department of Nature and Environmental Conservation of the Cape Provincial Administration, Cape Town.

Skinner, J.D. & Smithers, R.H.N. 1990. *The mammals of the southern African subregion*. University of Pretoria, Pretoria.

Snijman, D. 1984. A revision of the genus *Haemanthus* L. (Amaryllidaceae). *Journal of South African Botany* 12: 1–139.

Stewart, J., Linder, H.P., Schelpe, E.A. & Hall, A.V. 1982. *Wild orchids of southern Africa*. Macmillan, Johannesburg.

Steyn, P. 1982. *Birds of prey of southern Africa: their identification and life histories*. David Philip, Cape Town.

Steyn, P. 1984. *A delight of owls: African owls observed*. David Philip, Cape Town.

Stirton, C.H. (Ed.) 1978. *Plant invaders: beautiful but dangerous*. Department of Nature and Environmental Conservation of the Cape Provincial Administration, Cape Town.

Thunberg, C.P. 1795. *Travels in Europe, Africa and Asia performed between the years 1770 and 1774, Vols I–II*. Richardson & Egerton, London.

Van der Walt, J.J.A. & Vorster, P.J. 1977–1988. *Pelargoniums of southern Africa (Vols I–III)*. Purnell, Cape Town.

Van Riebeeck, J. 1958. *Journal of Jan van Riebeeck*. Thom, H.B. (Ed.) A.A. Balkema, Cape Town.

Vogts, M. 1982. *South Africa's Proteaceae: know them and grow them*. Struik, Cape Town.

Wager, V.A. 1986. *Frogs of South Africa: their fascinating life stories*. Delta Books, Johannesburg.

# Index

Page numbers in italic refer to photograph captions.

## STANDARD EDITION

HELEN ABBOTT
ABC BOOKSHOP
JOY ABRAHAMS
MRS BARBARA ANN ADAMS
HENRY & NADINE AIKMAN
J.F. AITCHISON
IVONNE & OSWALD ALBERS
DAVID & ANN ALSTON
ANTONIO FEDERICO ALZIATI
SEAN ARCHER
ELIZABETH ASHTON
PETER J. ASHTON
H. AUCAMP
H.E. AUSTEN
THE AVONDALE TRUST
MARILYN & JOHN BAILEY
PAOLETTA BAKER
DAVID & LINDA BALDIE
DARYL & SHARNA BALFOUR
DR DON BALL
FR R.H. BALL
N.E.C. BARLOW
E.A. BARRY
MICHAEL & AGNES BARRY
S.L. BARRY
W. BARSBY
THE BASSETT FAMILY
DUNCAN BATES, EAGLES REST FARM,
    CAPE POINT
PAT BAYLEY & BILL BOYD
F.M.A. BEAN
YVONNE BECKER
VAUGHAN & LINDA BECKERLING
CHRISTA BEE
MARK BEESTON
THOMAS BEHNISCH
KATHY, DERRICK & CAITLIN BELING
COLIN BELL
KATHERINE CLAUDIA BERCHTOLD
FIONA BERRISFORD & CHRISTOPHER
    BERENS
PETER & MARY ROSE BERRISFORD
KARIN BEYLEVELDT
CLIVE BIDEN
DR SUZANNE BISCHOFF
HILTON BLAKE
MICHAEL BLERSCH
JILL & PETER BLIGNAUT
MUNRO E. BLOCH
ROBERT WYNNE BLOUNT
GUDRUN & WOLF BOEMER
ISOBELLE & GORDON BOHLMANN
W.J. BOND
PETER BORCHERT
BOSSIE & ALET BOSMAN
BOTANICAL SOCIETY OF SOUTH
    AFRICA
ZELDA BOTMA
C. BOUCHER
GEORGES & CHRISTINE BOUCHER
ERIC BOURGOIN
DR O. BOURQUIN
DR & MRS PAUL BOWER
PROF. PAT BOWERBANK
JONATHAN BRAND
IRENE BREDENKAMP
MR & MRS HARRY BREWS
ROB & SHIRLEY BRICE-BRUCE
MRS S.J. BRINK
DAVID J. BRISTOW
GUY BROOKE-SUMNER
DENIS J. BROTHERS
DR PENNY BROWN & DR GUY
    PRESTON
RICHARD & RUTH BROWNE
M.A. BUTT
STEPHEN CAHILL
E.D. CAMPBELL
TOM CAMPBELL
HAROLD CARLESS
DAVE CARTER
LOUISE & RANDALL CARTER

REGINA CEMERNJAK
PHILIP & ALTHEA CHAMBERLAIN
M.J. & T.A. CHAPMAN
ELIZABETH CHAUNDY, IN MEMORY
    OF MAURICE
MRS P. CHRISTIE
CICLITIRA
P.J. CILLIÉ
A.J.L. CLARK
NIGEL & VAL CLAXTON
E.H.T. CLUVER
SONGVEI CLUVER
MEG COATES PALGRAVE
VANESSA COCKRAM
GODFREY & HELENE COETZEE
JOHANN & STEPH COETZEE
M.J.R. COETZEE
ANDREW COLLINS
L.A. COLLINS
M. COLLINS
NORMAN & CAROL COLLINS
ROBIN & HENRIETTA COLLINS
SUE COLLINS
I. CONRADIE
ROBERT COOKE
N.M.C. COOPER
HUGH & CATHERINE CORDER
ALAN CORTIE
GRAHAM, SHARYN, LEITH & JEREMY
    COUPLAND
G. & Y. COURTIN
GRAHAM & JILL COX
ANTON COY
DR S.A. CRAVEN
GAIL & LES CROOKES
BERIC & JUDY CROOME
PAUL CROSLAND
TIM & SANDY CUMMING
PADDY & NEVILLE DAVEY
TONY & HELEN DAVIDSON
R.W. DAY
SHELMERDENE DE GERSIGNY
DANIE EN MAGDA DE KLERK
D. DE MILANDER
MICHAEL DE NIER
ROB DE NIER
TOM DE ROO
LOUIS DE VILLIERS & RACHELLE
    GREEFF
BETTY & JAN DE VOS
MOLLY DE WET
DR NIC DE WET, SOMERSET WEST
WINNIE DEACON
SUSAN DEWE
MARTIN, LISA, VINCENT & MARCUS
    DI BELLA
LEICESTER DICEY
R.F. DILLAERTS
CAROLE & WILLIAM DIXON
KAREN V. DIXON
MAGGIE DIXON
R.A. & S.A. DIXON
ARTO DONIKYAN
JAMES DONOGHUE
GRAEME DOTT
JACK DRINKALL
NANNA DU TOIT
FRIEDA DUCKITT
MRS JUDITH DUDLEY
MAVIS DUFF
DAVID & JULIE DYER
J. GORDON DYER
LORRAINE EADY
LEON K. EADY
STEVE EALES
R.D. EDDIE
URS EGGLI
FRANK & CAROLYN EINHORN
ROBIN ELAM-RYE
DR JACK ELLIOTT
DAVID JOHN ELLIS
TREVOR & ANNE EMSLIE

ENCHANTED GARDEN, DIAL-A-PLANT,
    HOUT BAY
COLIN ENGEL
SCHALK ENGELBRECHT
MANFRED ENICKL
JESPER S. ERIKSEN
CARLA & FELIX ERNST
DAVID N. EVANS
GRAHAM EVANS
R.W.H. EVANS
MR C. & MRS T. EYERS
ELAINE EYRE
ELIZABETH FABER
DR A.G. FAGAN
FALCON COLLEGE, ZIMBABWE
IAN & CAROL FARLAM
PAULINE FARQUHAR
DR JILL FARRANT
J.L. FATTI
ALEXIUS FAURE
CONNIE FEAST
KHAKIE FERREIRA
SELMA A. FERREIRA
PETER B. FERRETT
THE FIEGGEN FAMILY
DR DAVID FIG
ADRIÉNNE FOLB & NORMAN
    MORRISON
D.J. FÖLSCHER
KIRBY W. FONG
PROF. & MRS ARDERNE FORDER
W.J. FORREST
PERE FRAGA I ARGVIMBAV
SUNA FRATER
DR S. FREEDBERG
RUSSEL, BONNIE & GABRIELLA
    FRIEDMAN
KEVIN & MARGERY GALLAGHER
MERVYN & ALLISON GANS
GREG GARDEN
KATHY GARRITY
PROF. NEIL GARROD
DAVID T. GEACH
DR H. GEERTSEMA
MARION GEIGER-ORENGO
COMM. U. GERICKE
DAVID & GABY GESS
SHIRLEY GETTLIFFE
HAROLD VERNON GIBBERD
MRS MARY S. GIBBONS
DOROTHEA E. GILL
KEN & MADELON GILLARD
BERNARD & MOLLY GILROY
P.J. GINN
DOT GLANVILL
IAN & ANNE GLASS
MEVAGH GLYN
PETER & TESSA GOEMANS
MARTHA GOING
MRS BETTY GOODCHILD
EVELYN GOODYEAR
MR & MRS J.D. GOODYEAR
MEL GOOTT
MAJOR I.A.D. GORDON MBE
NIKI GOULANDRIS, KIFISSIA, GREECE
G.L. GOULDING
MURRAY GRAHAM
CHRISTINE GRANT
ALLAN W.B. GRAY
DAVID GREENHALGH
KATHY GREENWOOD
ANTHONY GREGOROWSKI
THE GROBICKI FAMILY
JOHN & CAROL GROENEWALD
DR R.H. GROVES
MORITZ GRUBENMANN
THE GUTHRIES, DURBAN
MICK & LYNN HAIGH
COLIN HALL
DR ANTHONY HALL-MARTIN
IAN PAUL HALLIWELL
IZAK HANEKOM

CHARLES E. HARDMAN
ROBERT H. HARM
WOLF-GEORGE HARMS
JULIE HARRELL
JOHN F. HARRISON
HARRY MOLTENO LIBRARY, NATIONAL
    BOTANICAL INSTITUTE
J.O.C. HART
MR & MRS COLIN HARTLEY
THEO & CHRISTINE HARTWIG
JOHAN HAUSER
MAUREEN & HENK HAVINGA, PEIZE,
    NETHERLANDS
COLIN A.S. HAYNE
PEGGY HEARD
GEOFFREY A. HEDGECOCK
DOREEN & ROGER HEMP
HILMAR & ISOLDE HENDRICH
DOROTHEA HERBERT
HERSCHEL PREPARATORY SCHOOL
JANET E. HODGKISS
INGRID SOPHIE HOERSCH
JOHN & NAKKIE HOFFMAN
PIERRE & BRONWYN HOFMEYR
DIANA HOOD
CLIVE & SUZANNE HOOK
BIRGITTA HOPE
DR JOHN D. HOPTON
P.J. HOWISON
TIM & PAULA HOWSE
B.V.K. HUDSON
LINDSAY HUNT
C.R. HUNTING
L.R. HUNTING
M.S. HUNTING
IAN B. HUNTLEY
ERIKA HUNTLY
JOHN P. HURABIELL
A.C. HUTCHINSON
JANE & DOUG HUTSON
FRIEDRICH HÜTTEL, DORNBACH,
    AUSTRIA
JANE L. HUTTON
MEV H.J. HUYSAMEN
HAROLD IDESIS
JOHN ING
INSTITUTE FOR PLANT
    CONSERVATION
GEOFF & MYRLE IRONS
YOSHITO IWASA
J.W. JAGGER LIBRARY, UNIVERSITY OF
    CAPE TOWN
DAVID & ELSPETH JACK
STEPHEN L. JAFFE
DR & MRS W.I. JARDINE
R.G. JEFFERY
RALF JOHANNSEN
DR M.H. JOHANNSMEIER
BRIAN & WIN JOHNSON
D.D. JOOSTE
JUNE & ERIC JUDD
SIDNEY H. KAHN
J.M. KALMANSON
AMANDA KATZ
DEREK W. KEATS
M.F. KEELEY
MICHAEL & CLELIA KELLETT
ALIKI & CLIVE KELLY
E.W. KENT
JOHANN KIKILLUS
CLIVE S. KING
MICHAEL W. KING
A.R.W. KINTSCHER
DR MICHAEL W. KLEMENS
RICHARD KNIGHT
DAVID & NOLEEN KNOTT
WERNER E. KNUFFEL
JEN-FENG KO & SHENG-SHAN LU
JOZEF KOLLIN
LELLA KONDYLIS
DARYL & YOUSEF KOUTNIK &
    RANA TAYAR

SHIRLEY & ANDY KRAJEWSKI
JANE KRAUNSOE
MARK A. KRETSCHMER
FRANCI & MARIAAN KRONE
LYNETTE KRUGER
PIETER LABUSCHAGNE
CHRISTINE LANGENEGGER
A. LASCH
K.A.S. LATHAM
DR S.H. LAUBSCHER
FRANS LAURENS
DR TOM LAWSON
B.A. LAZARUS
MARY ANNE LE JEUNE
DR KARIN LECUONA
PAUL LEE
JOHN LENNARD
JEAN MARIE & ASTRI LEROY
MRS S.S.E. LEWIS
THALIA LINCOLN
EDWARD & ANDREA LINDSAY-
  BOWMAN
JILL LOCKLEY
MICHELINE LOGAN
MISS F.M. LOMBARD
R.M. LONGDEN-THURGOOD
ELMER J. LORENZ
ESTELLE LOTTER
PROF. JOHANN D. LOUBSER
BETTY LOUW
D.J. LOUW
SHELAGH LUBBOCK
DRS IAN & SUE MACDONALD
ANN & MARTIN MACGREGOR
VYVIAN MACGREGOR
N.W. MACKAY
O.J. MACKENZIE
JAMES MACPHAIL
YAKOOB M. MAKDA
DOROTHY E. MALAN
JOHANN H. MALAN EN GESIN
BILL & JEAN MALLEY
CHARLES MALTBY
SINJI MANATSU
D.S. MARAIS
RAUL MARQUES
DR T.C.H. MATHEWS
F.J. MATTHEWS
WINIFRED J. MCALISTER
HEATHER K. MCBURNIE
IAN MCCALL
KIM MCGREGOR
TERRI-LEE MCGREGOR
GEOFF MCILLERON
SEAN MCKEAG
TAMLYN MCKEAG
WENDY MCKEAG
DUNCAN MCKECHNIE
DAVID & KAREN MCLENNAN
CAMERON & RHODA MCMASTER
I.B. MCWALTER
MRS L. O. MEHMEL
DAVID MELUNSKY
MARGARET A. MEREDITH
ARLENE & ROBERT MIDDLEBROOK,
  USA
JONATHAN MILES
RITA MILLER
P.D. MINNAAR
MISSOURI BOTANICAL GARDEN
  LIBRARY
MISTY MOUNTAIN FARM,
  TSITSIKAMMA
JOHN D. MITCHELL
YASUSHIGE MIYAGAWA
BUDDY & JENNY MOCKFORD
MEGAN MOONEY
PATRICK MORANT
DR D.G. MORDANT
MICHAEL J. MORGAN
TERRI C. MORGAN
MILOU MORLION
ALISON MORPHET
MR M.C.W. MORRIS
ROBIN MOSER
ROS MUIRHEAD
DIRK MULLER

SONJA MULLER
TARA MUNRO
MRS. JUANITA MURRAY
PENNY MUSTART
NAMIBRAND NATURE RESERVE
PROF. W. DU T. NAUDÉ
CHRIS & ESTELLE NEETHLING
HYLTON NEL
NEW HANOVER SCHOOL
DR MARK NEW
DOUGLAS NEWTON
SARAH NEWTON
L-M. NICHOLLS
PETER NICOLAI
HANS NIEUWMEYER
NEIL NIGHTINGALE
MRS G.A. NIKSCHTAT
PATRICK NIVEN
MARILYN & TIMOTHY NOAKES
TRAVIS MILES NOAKES
CAREL A. NOLTE
GILLY & BAMBI NOTTEN
M.C. O'DOWD
S.H.H. OELOFSE
ALIDA & PETER OLDROYD
ONDERWYSKOLLEGE BOLAND
BELINDA OOSTHUIZEN
MR W.F. OOSTHUIZEN
ROBERT ORNDUFF
MAVIS ORPEN
DAVID L. ORTON
DAVID & TOPS OSBORN
CORA & CYRIL OVENS
R. PAMPEL
GIACOMO PAONESSA
DALE & ELIZABETH PARKER
RENÉE PARRY-DAVIES
MR & MRS J.M. PARSLEY
A.C. PASSMORE
JENNIFER & CHARL PAUW
MR HENRY PAYNE
PETER PENTZ
JEFFRY PERLMAN
PAULINE L. PERRY
CHRISTOPHER PETER
KATHLEEN PETERSEN
DAVID PICKERING
BEN J.P. PIENAAR, STELLENBOSCH
KEN & WENDY PINKERTON
ENG. MANUEL PITA, FUNCHAL,
  MADEIRA, PORTUGAL
DAVID PLANE
ROBIN A. PLUMBRIDGE
CARL & MARY LYNNE POHL
DR N. POLLEY
KEITH & MARILYN POOLE
THOMAS R. PRAY
DAVID S. PRELLER
O.W.E PRENTICE
MICHAEL LESLIE PURCELL
D.V. QUAIL
ADRIAN RADEMEYER
CHRIS RAINER-POPE
GUENTER RAZ, LANGENZERSDORF,
  AUSTRIA
ELAINE READ
MR & MRS G.H. READ & FAMILY
MARK READ
PHILIP E. READ
MRS DIANA REEKIE
MARTIN & BESSY REITZ
DAVE, CORLIA & SEAN RICHARDSON
G.V.C. RICHARDSON
MR & MRS R. RICHTER
BOB & ALISON RIGHTFORD
BERNARD W. RILEY
BEVERLEY ROBERTS
DOUGLAS STUART ROBERTS
SEAN C. ROBERTS
DUNCAN ROBERTSON
PAUL ROBINS
BASIL & SUE ROBINSON
ALAN G. ROLLASON
PAT ROOSE
DR & MRS J.B. ROSSITER
NIGEL ROSSOUW
MR & MRS T.E. ROTHWELL

NEVILLE ROWE
ROBERT M. RUBIN
F. ULRICH RUCH
MRS JOY RÜGER
DR & MRS A. RUPERT
DR ROBIN SANDELL
M.D. SANDERS
ROB & CHRISTINE SATCHEL
H.L. SCHAARY
J.E.C. SCHACKIS
DR H.J.W.G. SCHALKE, OEGSTGEEST,
  NETHERLANDS
SYBELLA SCHELPE
CLAUDIA SCHRANER
ROBERT SCHRANER
MRS P.M. SCHREINER
JONATHAN SCHRIRE
DAVID M. SCHULTZ
DENZIL & GAY SCHWULST
MICHAEL & DOREEN SCOTT
J.M.C. SCULLY
M.V.C. SCULLY
R.J.C. SCULLY
GILL & MERVYN SEGAL
FREDERICK R. SELLMAN, LONDON
BO & ANTHEA SERRITSLEV
EDUARD SEVENSTER
DR R. SÉVIN, LAUSANNE
T. SHAW
MR & MRS LOUIS SHILL
A-D. SHOLTO-DOUGLAS
RUTH SIEBOLDT
SALLY SILBERBAUER
PETER & LIZZY SIMON
WILLY, WENDY, ROBERT & LIZA SIMON
MARY SIMONS
A.R.M. SIMPSON
MARK SIMPSON
GENARD RUSSEL WILLIAM SIZER
GERD W. SKALA
GEORGINA SKINNER
MICHAEL SLAYEN
H.L. SLOMOWITZ
MRS BARBARA SMALLWOOD
C.A. & E.M. SMITH
HENK SMITH
JEAN SMITH
PETER R. SOUTHEY
ROSEMARY SMUTS
H.W. SNIBBE
JENS SONDERGAARD
SOUTH AFRICAN COLLEGE HIGH
  SCHOOL
ARCHIE SPROTT
ST MARY'S SCHOOL, WAVERLEY,
  JOHANNESBURG
H. STALLING
JOHN I. STANSBURY
A.N. STARKE
INES & BASIL STATHOULIS
JAN & ANN STEKHOVEN
THEO STEWART
J.H. STEYN
PETER STEYN
BOB & MARY STOBIE
DORIS STRAUS
LEONORE STROBOS
TERRI & JOLENE STUPEL
DR NIKO STUTTERHEIM
DIEDRICH SUPTHUT
SUTHERLAND HIGH SCHOOL
ELIZABETH SUTTIE
MR J.C. & MRS D.L. SWANEPOEL
KATHLEEN TACON
ERNST TAEUBER
HIROVUKI TANABE
NORMAN TATE
C. & D. TAUTE
J.C. & L. TAYLOR
MRS J. TERRY-LLOYD
DR WALTHER THIEDE
HEINZ HERMAN THIELE
DIANA THOMPSON
THE THOMPSON FAMILY
GRACE N. THOMPSON
RICHARD THOMPSON
ALAN & DIANA THOMSON

G. TOBIAS
RICHARD & JUDITH TODD
G.P. TOERIEN
CAROL CORWIN TORGESON
DAVE & JO TRICKETT
ELIZABETH TRIEGAARDT
ROD TRITTON
JOHN, ROSEANNE & CAITLIN TURNER
MRS JOHN G. TURNER
DR & MRS J.C. TYRRELL
PRIMROSE & MICHAEL UPWARD
MRS W.E. UŸS
EVA VAN BELLE
J.P. VAN BELLE
H.D. VAN BOHEMEN, NETHERLANDS
DR ERIKA VAN DEN BERG
HETTIE VAN DEN BERGH
ELEANORE VAN DER HORST
JOHANNES VAN DER HORST
K.C. VAN DER HOVEN
DICK & LIZ VAN DER JAGT
BETH VAN DER LINDE
DR ROELOF VAN DER MERWE
PHILIP VAN DER SPUY
NEIL & YVETTE VAN DER WEELE
PROF. LEON VAN DONGEN
ANNE & ERROL VAN GREUNEN
RICHARD & DRIENIE VAN NIEKERK
SIMON VAN NOORT
MRS T.A.M. VAN OGTROP
OSCAR VAN OORDT
M. & M.A. VAN RIJSWIJCK
A.J. VAN RYNEVELD
JOHANN L. VAN SCHALKWYK
PAUL VAN SCHALKWYK
WILLIE VAN SCHOOR
A.W. VAN VLAANDEREN
MARIUS & LENETTE VAN WYK
DR PAUL LOEB VAN ZUILENBURG
R. VAN ZYL-SMIT
ANDRÉ VAN DEN BAVIÈRE
SUSAN EN VELLIES VELDSMAN
MAIK VESTE, UNIVERSITY OF
  BIELEFELD, GERMANY
DANIEL & MABEL VISSER
MARIETJIE EN TIAAN VISSER
ETIENNE & SUSANN VLOK
HANS RUEDI VOGEL
W.H. VOIGT
YVONNE SCHROEDER VON HAGEN
RALPH VON KNOBLAUCH
KLAUS VON LUDWIGER
JENNY WAINWRIGHT-KLEIN
G.L. WALDEN
DAVID & FELICITY WALKER
LINDSAY & GAIL WALKER
CHARLIE WARD
THE WARD FAMILY
NILS ERIK WARNER
ERIKA WATSON
PROF. IAN B. WATT
KERRY WEBB
P.T. WEDEPOHL
THEODORE & NICOLETTE WEICKER
JILL WEINBERG
M.C. WENT-SCHULTZ
WESSEL P. WESSELS
WESTERFORD HIGH SCHOOL
WESTERN PROVINCE PREPARATORY
  SCHOOL
WOLFGANG WETSCHNIG
MR ROD WHITE
MRS I. WHITELOCK
A.G. WHITFIELD
CLARE WICKMAN
SALLY WIGLEY
DR A.R. WIJNBERG
BRYAN & PRISCILLA WILLIAMS
TIMOTHY J. WILLIAMS
B.C. WINKLER
ANETTE WODRICH
MARK WOODLAND
BERIC WRIGHT
ALAN YATES & AMELI TRANTINA-
  YATES
JOHN YELD
MAURICE ZUNCKEL